OPERATION, MAINTENANCE AND REPAIR OF AUXILIARY GENERATORS

US ARMY
US NAVY

Fredonia Books
Amsterdam, The Netherlands

Operation, Maintenance and Repair of Auxiliary
Generators

by
U.S. Army
U.S. Navy

ISBN: 1-4101-0824-4

Reprinted from the 1996 edition

Fredonia Books
Amsterdam, The Netherlands
http://www.fredoniabooks.com

Army Technical Manual
No. 5-685
Navy Manual
No. NAVFAC MO-912

TM 5-685
NAVFAC MO-912

HEADQUARTERS
DEPARTMENTS OF THE ARMY AND THE NAVY
Washington, DC, *26 August 1996*

OPERATION, MAINTENANCE AND REPAIR OF AUXILIARY GENERATORS

LIST OF FIGURES

LIST OF TABLES

CHAPTER 1

INTRODUCTION

1-1. Purpose.

This manual covers the various types of auxiliary power generating systems used on military installations. It provides data for the major components of these generating systems; such as, prime movers, generators, and switchgear. It includes operation of the auxiliary generating system components and the routine maintenance which should be performed on these components. It also describes the functional relationship of these components and the supporting equipment within the complete system.

1-2. Scope.

The guidance and data in this manual are intended to be used by operating, maintenance, and repair personnel. It includes operating instructions, standard inspections, safety precautions, troubleshooting, and maintenance instructions. The information applies to reciprocating (diesel) and gas turbine prime movers, power generators, switchgear, and subsidiary electrical components. It also covers fuel, air, lubricating, cooling, and starting systems.

a. In addition to the information contained in this manual, power plant engineers, operators, and maintenance personnel must have access to all other literature related to the equipment in use. This includes military and commercial technical manuals and engineering data pertaining to their particular plant.

b. Appendixes B through F provide details related to fuel storage, lubricating oil, coolant, forms and records, and safety (including first aid). Texts and handbooks are valuable tools for the trained engineer, supervisor, and operator of a power plant. The manufacturers of the components publish detailed operating, maintenance, and repair manuals. Instructions, applicable to the equipment, are provided by each manufacturer and should be filed at the plant for safekeeping and use. Replacement copies are available from each manufacturer.

1-3. References.

Appendix A contains a list of references used in this manual. Other pertinent literature may be substituted or used as supplements.

1-4. Explanation of abbreviations and terms.

Abbreviations and special terms used in this manual are explained in the glossary.

CHAPTER 2

EMERGENCY POWER SYSTEMS

2-1. Emergency power.

Emergency power is defined as an independent reserve source of electric energy which, upon failure or outage of the normal source, automatically provides reliable electric power within a specified time.

a. A reliable and adequate source of electric power is necessary for the operation of active military installations. Power must also be available at inactive installations to provide water for fire protection, energy for automatic fire alarms, light for security purposes, heat for preservation of critical tactical communications and power equipment, and for other operations.

b. Power, supplied by either the local utility company or generated on-site, is distributed over the activity. The source of distribution may be subject to brownout, interruption or extended outage. Mission, safety, and health requirements may require an uninterruptible power supply (UPS) or standby/emergency supply for specific critical loads. Justifiable applications for auxiliary generator are:

(1) Hospitals (life support, operating room, emergency lighting and communication, refrigeration, boiler plant, etc.).

(2) Airfields (control tower, communications, traffic control, engine start, security, etc.).

(3) Data processing plant systems.

(4) Critical machinery

(5) Communication and security.

c. It is essential that a schematic showing the loads to be carried by an auxiliary generator be available for reference. Do not add loads until it is approved by responsible authority.

2-2. Types of power generation sources.

a. The critical uses of electric power at a site demand an emergency source of power whenever an outage occurs. Selection of the type of auxiliary generating plant is based on the mission of the particular site and its anticipated power consumption rate during an emergency. The cost of plant operation (fuel, amortized purchase price, depreciation, and insurance) and operation and maintenance personnel requirements must be analyzed. Future load growth requirements of the site must be considered for size selection.

b. Auxiliary power generating plants are designated as either class B or class C. The design criteria for a class B plant is comparable to those of a primary power plant. A primary power plant usu-

ally is started manually; a class B plant may have either a manual or an automatic start system. Accordingly, a class B plant is almost as costly to construct and operate as a primary power plant of similar size. Usually, a class B plant is a permanent-type unit capable of operating between 1000 and 4000 hours annually. The class C plant always has an autostart control system (set to start the plant when the primary power voltage varies or the frequency changes more than the specified operational requirements).

(1) A class B plant (considered a standby long-term power source) is used where multiple commercial power feeders are not available or extended and frequent power outages may occur. Total fuel storage must be enough for at least 15 days continuous operation.

(2) A class C plant is used where rapid restoration of power is necessary to feed the load. More than one class C unit is usually used when the technical load exceeds 300 kW at 208Y/120 volts or 600 kilowatts (kW) at 480Y/277 volts. Spare class C units are sometimes provided for rotational maintenance service. The autostart control system ensures that the load is assumed as rapidly as possible. Diesel engine prime movers may be equipped with coolant and lubricating oil heaters to ensure quick starting. Recommended total fuel storage must be enough for at least seven days continuous operation.

c. Emergency generators must provide adequate power for critical loads of a building or a limited group of buildings, heating plants, utility pumping plant, communication centers, or other such installations where interruption of normal service would be serious enough to justify installation of an auxiliary power plant. The plant must be reliable and easily started in all seasons of the year. The plant building should be completely fireproof with heating and ventilation facilities that satisfy the plant's requirements. The space around the units should permit easy access for maintenance and repair. Space should be provided within the building for safe storage of fuel such as a grounded and vented "day" tank. Type and grade of fuel should be identified on the tank. Important considerations for these plants included the following:

(1) Selection of generators (size and quantity, type of prime mover, and load requirements).

(2) Determination of need for instrumentation (meters, gauges, and indicator lights).

(3) Selection of protective equipment (relays and circuit breakers).

(4) Determination of need for automatic starters, automatic load transfer, etc.

(5) Selection of auxiliary generator size is based on satisfying the defined electrical load requirement (expressed as kilowatts).

d. Portable power plants are widely used on military installations because of the temporary nature of many applications. The power plants (including a diesel or gas turbine prime mover) are self-contained and mounted on skids, wheels, or semi-trailers. Although the size of portable units may vary from less than 1 kW to more than 1,000 kW, the most commonly used units are less than 500 kW capacity. Reciprocating prime movers are usually used for portable power plants. Gas turbine engines are frequently employed for smaller units because of their relatively light weight per horsepower.

e. Portable diesel powered generators usually operate at 1200, 1800 or 3600 revolutions per minute (rpm), since high speeds allow a reduction in weight of the generator plant. To keep weight down, such ancillary equipment as voltage regulators, electric starters and batteries are sometimes omitted from the smaller generators. Starting may be done by crank or rope, ignition by magneto, and voltage regulation through air-gap, pole-piece, and winding design. Portable plants usually have a minimum number of meters and gauges. Larger size portable units have an ammeter, a frequency meter, a voltmeter, and engine temperature and oil pressure gauges. Generator protection is obtained by fused switches or air circuit breakers.

2-3. Buildings and enclosures.

a. Auxiliary power generating equipment, especially equipment having standby functions, should be provided with suitable housings. A typical power plant installation is shown in figure 2-1. The equipment should be located as closely as possible to the load to be served. Generators, prime movers, switchboards, and associated switching equipment should always be protected from the environment. Many small units are designed for exterior use and have their own weatherproof covering. Transformers and high-voltage switching equipment can be placed outdoors if they are designed with drip-proof enclosures.

b. The buildings housing large auxiliary power generating systems (see fig 2-1) require adequate ceiling height to permit installation and removal of cylinder heads, cylinder liners, pistons, etc., using chain falls. An overhead I-beam rail, or movable structure that will support a chain fall hoist, is necessary. The building should have convenience outlets and be well lighted with supplemental lighting for instrument panels. Heat for the building should be steam, heat pumps or electric heaters to avoid hazards from explosive vapors.

c. Prime movers require a constant supply of large quantities of air for combustion of fuel. Combustion produces exhaust gases that must be removed from the building since the gases are hazardous and noxious. The air is usually supplied via a louvered ventilation opening. Exhaust gases are conducted to the outside by piping that usually includes a silencer or muffler (see fig 2-1).

d. Precautions must be taken when environmental conditions related to location of the generating system are extreme (such as tropical heat and/or desert dryness and dust). Cooling towers and special air filters are usually provided to combat these conditions. Arctic conditions require special heating requirements.

e. When required for the auxiliary generating equipment, the building or enclosure should be fireproof and constructed of poured concrete or concrete and cinder blocks with a roof of reinforced concrete, steel, or wood supports with slate or other fireproof shingles. Ventilation and openings for installation and removal of materials and equipment should be provided.

(1) *Foundations.* A generator and its prime mover should be set on a single, uniform foundation to reduce alignment problems. The foundation should be in accordance with manufacturer's recommendations for proper support of equipment and dampening of vibrations. Foundation, prime mover, and generator should be mechanically isolated from the building floor and structure to eliminate transmission of vibrations. All mechanical and electrical connections should allow for vibration isolation.

(2) *Floors.* The floors are usually concrete with non-skid steel plates over cable and fuel-line trenches. The floor space should provide for servicing, maintenance, work benches, repair parts, tool cabinets, desks, switchboard, and electrical equipment. Battery bank areas require protection from corrosive electrolytes. Floors must be sealed to prevent dusting, absorption of oils and solvents, and to promote cleanliness and ease of cleanup. Plates and gratings covering floor trenches must be grounded. Rubber matting should be installed in front of and around switchboards and electrical equipment to minimize shock hazard.

2-4. Fuel storage.

Fuel storage space should be provided near the plant, with enough capacity to allow replenishment in economical, reasonable intervals. The total fuel storage capacity should be large enough to satisfy

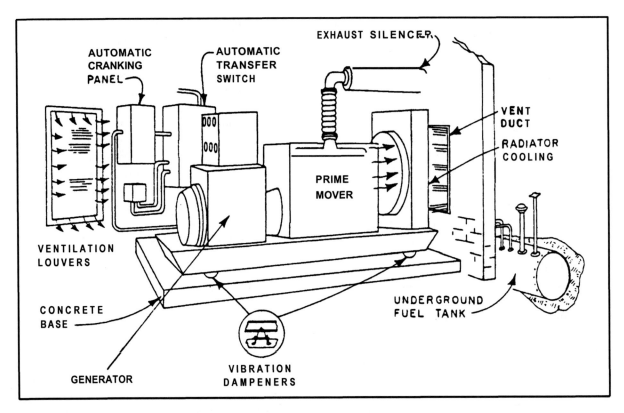

Figure 2-l. Typical installation of an emergency power plant.

the operational requirements of the class B or class C generating plants that are used. Fuel logistics should be considered when sizing fuel storage capacity

a. Fuels for the equipment described herein (refer to app C) are combustible substances that can be burned in an atmosphere of oxygen. Two categories of fuel storage are discussed: liquids and gases. In either case, fuel storage tanks, associated pumps and piping systems must be grounded and protected from galvanic, stray current or environmental corrosion.

b. Liquid fuel for auxiliary power generating systems is usually stored in buried tanks equipped with vent pipes and manholes. Above-ground tanks may be used for storage at some locations. These tanks usually have provisions for venting, filling and cleaning. A gauge with indicator is used to determine tank contents. Two tanks are necessary to ensure a continuous supply during tank cleaning (every two years) and maintenance operations. Provisions must be made to use a gauge stick to positively determine depth of tank contents. Storage tanks should be checked for settled water accumulated through condensation and the free water drained periodically.

c. Gaseous fuel is stored in tanks either as a gas or a liquid, depending on the type of fuel. Natural gas is stored as a gas. Butane and propane are cooled and kept under moderate pressure for stor-age as liquids. Methods to determine tank contents are covered in paragraph 5-7*b*(8).

d. Day tanks. A grounded and vented day tank, having not more than 275 gallons capacity, is installed within the power plant building. The tank is normally filled by transfer pump from the installation's main storage tank. Provision should be made to fill the day tank by alternate means (or directly from safety cans or barrels) if the transfer system fails.

2-5. Loads.

Most electrical plants serve a varied load of lighting, heating equipment, and power equipment, some of which demand power day and night. The annual load factor of a well-operated installation will be 50 percent or more with a power factor of 80 percent or higher. Equipment and controls must be selected to maintain frequency and voltage over the load range.

2-6. Distribution systems.

a. The load determines direct current (DC) or alternating current (AC), voltage, frequency (DC, 25 Hertz (Hz), 50 Hz, 60 Hz, 400 Hz), phases and AC configuration (delta or wye). Voltage and other parameters of the distribution system will have been selected to transmit power with a minimum of conversion (AC to DC), inversion (DC to AC), (AC) transformer, impedance, and resistance loss. For a given load; higher voltage, unity power factor, low resistance/impedance, and lower frequency generally result in lower distribution losses. Use of equipment to change or regulate voltage, frequency or phase introduces resistance, hysteresis and mechanical losses.

b. A lagging power factor due to inductive loads (especially under-loaded induction motors) results in resistive losses (I^2R) because greater current is required for a given power level. This may be corrected by the use of capacitors at the station bus or by "run" capacitors at induction motors to have the generator "see" a near-unity but yet lagging power factor.

c. Overcorrection, resulting in a leading (capacitive) power factor must be avoided. This condition results in severe switching problems and arcing at contacts. Switching transients (voltage spikes, harmonic transients) will be very damaging to insulation, controls and equipment. The electronics in radio, word and data processing, and computer arrays are especially sensitive to switching and lighting transients, over/under voltage and frequency changes.

d. The distribution system must include sensing devices, breakers, and isolation and transfer feed switches to protect equipment and personnel.

2-7. Frequency.

The frequency required by almost all electrical loads is the standard 50 or 60 Hz. Most electrical equipment can operate satisfactorily when the frequency varies plus or minus ten percent ($\pm10\%$). Steady state frequency tolerance (required for frequency-sensitive electronic equipment) should not exceed plus or minus 0.5 percent of design frequency. Since some equipment are sensitive to frequency changes, operators must closely monitor frequency meters and regulate frequency when necessary.

2-8. Grounding.

Grounding implies an intentional electrical connection to a reference conducting plane, which may be earth (hence the term ground) but more generally consists of a specific array of interconnected electrical conductors referred to as grounding conductors. The term "grounding" as used in electric power systems indicates both system grounding and equipment grounding, which are different in their objectives.

a. System grounding relates to a connection from the electric power system conductors to ground for the purpose of securing superior performance qualities in the electric system. There are several methods of system grounding. System grounding ensures

longer insulation life of generators, motors, transformers, and other system components by suppressing transient and sustained overvoltages associated with certain fault conditions. In addition, system grounding improves protective relaying by providing fast, selective isolation of ground faults.

b. Equipment grounding, in contrast to system grounding, relates to the manner in which noncurrent-carrying metal parts of the wiring system or apparatus, which either enclose energized conductors or are adjacent thereto, are to be interconnected and grounded. The objectives of equipment grounding are:

(1) To ensure freedom from dangerous electric shock-voltage exposure to persons.

(2) To provide current-carrying capability during faults without creating a fire or explosive hazard.

(3) To contribute to superior performance of the electric system.

c. Many personal injuries are caused by electric shock as a result of making contact with metallic members that are normally not energized and normally can be expected to remain non-energized. To minimize the voltage potential between noncurrent-carrying parts of the installation and earth to a safe value under all systems operations (normal and abnormal), an installation grounding plan is required.

d. System grounding. There are many methods of system grounding used in industrial and commercial power systems (refer to fig 2-2), the major ones being:

(1) Ungrounded.

(2) Solidly grounded.

(3) Resistance grounding: low-resistance, high-resistance.

(4) Reactance grounding.

e. Technically, there is no generally accepted use of any one particular method. Each type of system grounding has advantages and disadvantages. Factors which influence the choice of selection include:

(1) Voltage level of the power system.

(2) Transient overvoltage possibilities.

(3) Type of equipment on the system.

(4) Cost of equipment.

(5) Required continuity of service.

(6) Quality of system operating personnel.

(7) Safety considerations, including fire hazard and others

f. An ungrounded system is a system in which there is no intentional connection between the neutral or any phase and ground. "Ungrounded system" literally implies that the system is capacitively coupled to ground.

(1) The neutral potential of an ungrounded system under reasonably balanced load conditions will

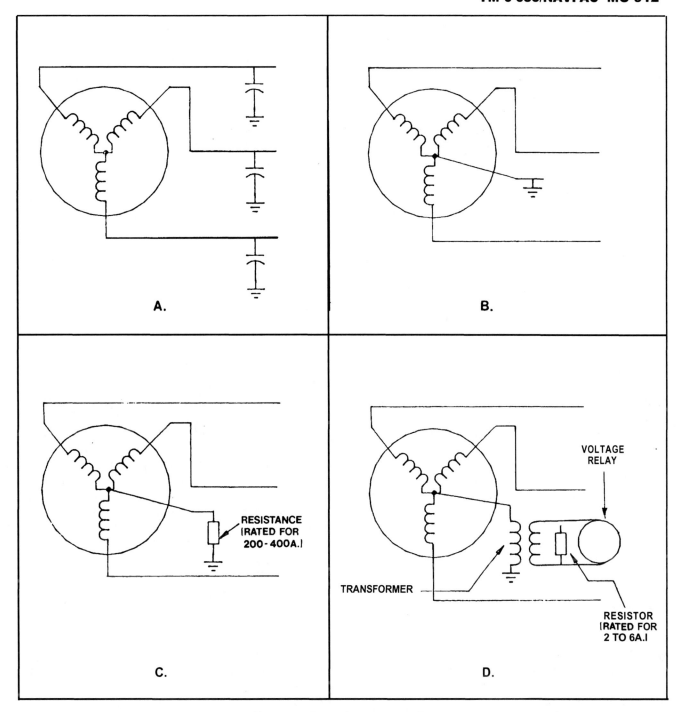

Figure 2-2. Types of system grounding.
A) UNGROUNDED GENERATOR, B) SOLIDLY GROUNDED, C) LOW RESISTANCE GROUNDING,
D) HIGH RESISTANCE GROUNDING

be close to ground potentials because of the capacitance between each phase conductor and ground. When a line-to-ground fault occurs on an ungrounded system, the total ground fault current is relatively small, but the voltage to ground potential on the unfaulted phases can reach an unprecedented value. If the fault is sustained, the normal line-to-neutral voltage on the unfaulted phases is increased to the system line-to-line voltage (i.e., square root of three (3) times the normal line-to-neutral value). Over a period of time this breaks down the line-to-neutral insulation and results in insulation failure. Ungrounded system operation is not recommended because of the high probability of failures due to transient over-voltages (especially in medium voltage i.e., 1 kilovolt (Kv)-15 Kv) caused by restriking ground faults.

(2) Overvoltage limitation is particularly important in systems over 1 Kv, because equipment in these voltage classes are designed with less margin between 50/60 Hz test and operating voltages than low voltage equipment. The remaining various grounding methods can be applied on system grounding protection depending on technical and economic factors. The one advantage of an ungrounded system that needs to be mentioned is that it generally can continue to operate under a single line-to-ground fault without significant damage to electrical equipment and without an interruption of power to the loads.

g. A solidly grounded system refers to a system in which the neutral, or occasionally one phase, is connected to ground without an intentional intervening impedance. On a solidly grounded system, in contrast to an ungrounded system, a ground fault on one phase will result in a large magnitude of ground current flow but there will be no increase in voltage on the unfaulted phase.

(1) On low-voltage systems (1 Kv and below), the National Electrical Code (NEC) Handbook, article 250-5(b) requires that the following class of systems be solidly grounded:

(a) Where the system can be so grounded that the maximum voltage to ground on the ungrounded conductors does not exceed 150 volts.

(b) Where the system is 3 phase, 4 wire wye connected in which the neutral is used as a circuit conductor.

(c) Where the system is 3 phase, 4 wire delta connected in which the midpoint of one phase winding is used as a circuit conductor.

(d) Where a grounded service conductor is uninsulated in accordance with the exceptions to NEC articles 230-22, 230-30, and 230-41.

(2) Solid grounding is mainly used in low-voltage distribution systems (less than 1000 volt (V) system) and high-voltage transmission systems (over 15 Kv). It is seldom used in medium-voltage systems (1 Kv to 15 Kv). Solid grounding has the lowest initial cost of all grounding methods. It is usually recomrrended for overhead distribution systems supplying transformers protected by primary fuses. However, it is not the preferred scheme for most industrial and commercial systems, again because of the severe damage potential of high-magnitude ground fault currents.

(3) In most generators, solid grounding may permit the maximum ground fault current from the generator to exceed the maximum 3-phase fault current which the generator can deliver and for which its windings are braced. This situation occurs when the reactance of the generator is large in comparison to the system reactance. National Electrical Manufacturers Association 1-78 places a requirement on the design of synchronous generators that their windings shall be braced to withstand the mechanical forces resulting from a bolted 3-phase short circuit at the machine terminals. The current created by a phase-to-ground fault occurring close to the generator will usually exceed the 3-phase bolted fault current. Due to the high cost of generators, the long lead time for replacement, and system impedance characteristics, a solidly grounded neutral is not recommended for generators rated between 2.4 Kv and 15 Kv.

(4) Limiting the available ground fault current by resistance grounding is an excellent way to reduce damage to equipment during ground fault conditions, and to eliminate personal hazards and electrical fire dangers. It also limits transient overvoltages during ground fault conditions. The resistor can limit the ground fault current to a desired level based on relaying needs.

h. Low-resistance grounding refers to a system in which the neutral is grounded through a considerably smaller resistance than used for high-resistance grounding. The resistor limits ground fault current magnitudes to reduce the damage during ground faults. The magnitude of the grounding resistance is selected to detect and clear the faulted circuit. Low-resistance grounding is used mainly on medium voltage systems (i.e., 2.4 Kv to 15 Kv), especially those which have directly connected rotating apparatus. Low-resistance grounding is not used on low-voltage systems, because the limited available ground fault current is insufficient to positively operate series trip units.

(1) Low-resistance grounding normally limits the ground fault currents to approximately 100 to 600 amps (A). The amount of current necessary for selective relaying determines the value of resistance to be used.

(2) At the occurrence of a line-to-ground fault on a resistance-grounded system, a voltage appears across the resistor which nearly equals the normal line-to-neutral voltage. of the system. The resistor current is essentially equal to the current in the fault. Therefore, the current is practically equal to the line-to-neutral voltage divided by the number of ohms of resistance used.

i. High-resistance grounding is a system in which the neutral is grounded through a predominantly resistive impedance whose resistance is selected to allow a ground fault current through the resistor equal to or slightly more than the capacitive charging current (i.e., $I_R > 3I_{co}$) of the system. The resistor can be connected either directly from neutral to ground for wye type systems where a system neutral point exists, or in the secondary circuit of a grounding transformer for delta type systems where a system neutral point does not exist. However, because grounding through direct high-resistance entails having a large physical resistance size with a continuous current rating (bulky and very costly), direct high-resistance grounding is not practical and would not be recommended. High-resistance grounding through a grounding transformer is cost effective and accomplishes the same objective.

(1) High-resistance grounding accomplishes the advantages of ungrounded and solidly grounded systems and eliminates the disadvantages. It limits transient overvoltages resulting from single phase to ground fault, by limiting ground fault currents to approximately 8 A. This amount of ground fault current is not enough to activate series over-current protective devices, hence no loss of power to downstream loads will occur during ground fault conditions.

(2) Special relaying must be used on a high-resistance grounded system in order to sense that a ground fault has occurred. The fault should then be located and removed as soon as possible so that if another ground fault occurs on either of the two unfaulted phases, high magnitude ground fault currents and resulting equipment damage will not occur.

(3) High-resistance grounding is normally applied on electrical systems rated 5kV and below. It is usually applied in situations where:

(a) It is essential to prevent unplanned system power outages.

(b) Previously the system has been operated ungrounded and no ground relaying has been installed.

(4) NEC Articles 250-5 Exception No. 5 and 250-27 have specific requirements for high impedance grounding for system voltages between 480 and 1000 V. For those system voltages the following criteria apply:

(a) The conditions of maintenance and supervision assure that only qualified persons will service the installation.

(b) Continuity of power is required.

(c) Ground detectors are installed on the system.

(d) Line-to-neutral loads are not served.

(5) Depending on the priority of need, high resistance grounding can be designed to alarm only or provide direct tripping of generators off line in order to prevent fault escalation prior to fault locating and removal. High-resistance grounding (arranged to alarm only) has proven to be a viable grounding mode for 600 V and 5 kV systems with an inherent total system charging current to ground ($3I_{co}$) of about 5.5 A or less, resulting in a ground fault current of about 8 A or less. This, however, should not be construed to mean that ground faults of a magnitude below this level will always allow the successful location and isolation before escalation occurs. Here, the quality and the responsiveness of the plant operators to locate and isolate a ground fault is of vital importance. To avoid high transient overvoltages, suppress harmonics and allow adequate relaying, the grounding transformer and resistor combination is selected to allow current to flow that is equal to or greater than the capacitive charging current.

j. Ground fault current can be reduced in distribution systems which are predominantly reactive through reactance grounding. A reactor is connected between the generator neutral and ground. The magnitude of the ground fault is directly related to the reactor size. The reactor should be sized such that the current flow through it is at least 25 percent and preferably 60 percent of the three phase fault current. Because of the high level of ground fault current relative to resistance grounded systems, reactance grounded systems are only used on high reactance distribution systems.

k. Whether to group or individually ground generators is a decision the engineer is confronted with when installing generator grounding equipment. Generators produce slightly non-sinusoidal voltage waveforms, hence, circulating harmonic currents are present when two or more generating units with unequal loading or dissimilar electrical characteristics are operated in parallel.

(1) The path for harmonic current is established when two or more generator neutrals are grounded, thus providing a loop for harmonic circulation. Because of the 120" relationship of other harmonics, only triple series (3rd, 9th, 15th, etc.) harmonic currents can flow in the neutral. Harmonic current problems can be prevented by: eliminating zero sequence loops (undergrounding the generator neutrals); providing a large impedance in the zero sequence circuit to limit circulating currents to tolerable levels (low or high resistance grounding the generator neutrals); connecting the generator neutrals directly to the paralleling switchgear neutral bus and grounding the bus at one point only; or, grounding only one generator neutral of a parallel system.

(2) An effective ground grid system in power plants or substations is highly important and one that deserves careful analysis and evaluation. The primary function of a ground grid is to limit voltages appearing across insulation, or between supposedly non-energized portions of equipment or structures within a person's reach under ground fault conditions. Reducing the hazard ensures the

safety and well being of plant personnel or the public at large. A ground grid system should also provide a significantly low resistance path to ground and have the capability to minimize rise in ground potential during ground faults.

(3) The conductive sheath or armor of cables and exposed conductive material (usually sheet metal) enclosing electrical equipment or conductors (such as panelboards, raceways, busducts, switchboards, utilization equipment, and fixtures) must be grounded to prevent electrical shock. All parts of the grounding system must be continuous.

(4) Personnel should verify that grounding for the system is adequate by performing ground resistance tests.

(5) The ground grid of the plant should be the primary system. In some cases a metallic underground water piping system may be used in lieu of a plant ground grid, provided adequate galvanic and stray current corrosion protection for the piping is installed, used and tested periodically. This practice is not acceptable in hazardous areas and is not recommended if the piping system becomes sacrificial.

(6) The plant ground grid should have a system resistance of 10 ohms or less. Ground grid system resistance may be decreased by driving multiple ground electrode rods. A few rods, deeply driven and widely spaced, are more effective than a large number of short, closely spaced rods. Solid hard copper rods should be used, not copperplated steel. When low resistance soils are deep, the surface extension rods may be used to reach the low resistance stratum. Bonding of ground conductors to rods should be by permanent exothermic weld (preferred) or compression sleeve, and not by bolted clamp (corrosion results in high resistance connection). Resistance at each rod in a multiple system should not exceed 15 ohms.

(7) Reliable ground fault protection requires proper design and installation of the grounding system. In addition, routine maintenance of circuit protective equipment, system grounding, and equipment grounding is required (refer to ground resistance testing, chap 7).

(8) Equipment grounding refers to the method in which conductive enclosures, conduits, supports, and equipment frames are positively and permanently interconnected and connected to the grounding system. Grounding is necessary to protect personnel from electric shock hazards, to provide adequate ground fault current-carrying capability and to contribute to satisfactory performance of the electrical system. Electrical supporting structures within the substation (i.e., metal conduit, metal

cable trays, metal enclosures, etc.) should be electrically continuous and bonded to the protective grounding scheme. Continuous grounding conductors such as a metallic raceway or conduit or designated ground wires should always be run from the ground grid system (i.e., location of generators) to downstream distribution switchboards to ensure adequate grounding throughout the electrical distribution system. Permanent grounding jumper cables must effectively provide a ground current path to and around flexible metallic conduit and removable meters. Shielded cables must be grounded per manufacturers' requirements. Shielded coaxial cable requires special grounding depending on use and function. A voltmeter must be used for detecting potential differences across the break in a bonding strap or conductor before handling.

(9) A typical grounding system for a building containing heavy electrical equipment and related apparatus is shown in figure 2-3. The illustration shows the following:

(a) Grounding electrodes (driven into the earth) to maintain ground potential on all connected conductors. This is used to dissipate (into the earth) currents conducted to the electrodes.

(b) Ground bus (forming a protective grounding network) which is solidly connected to the grounding electrodes.

(c) Grounding conductors (installed as necessary) to connect equipment frames, conduits, cable trays, enclosures, etc., to the ground bus.

(10) Radio frequency interference (RFI) is interference of communications transmission and reception caused by spurious emissions. These can be generated by communications equipment, switching of DC power circuits or operations of AC generation, transmission, and power consumers. The frequencies and sources of RFI can be determined by tests. Proper enclosures, shielding and grounding of AC equipment and devices should eliminate RFI. RFI can be carried by conductive material or be broadcast. Lamp ballasts, off-spec radio equipment and certain controls may be the prime suspects. The radio engineer or technician can trace and recommend actions to eliminate or suppress the emissions. Pickup of RFI can also be suppressed by increasing the separation distance between power and communication conductor runs.

2-9. Load shedding.

Load shedding is sometimes required during emergency situations or while operating from an auxiliary power source in order to ensure enough power gets to the critical circuits (such as the circuits required for classified communications or aircraft

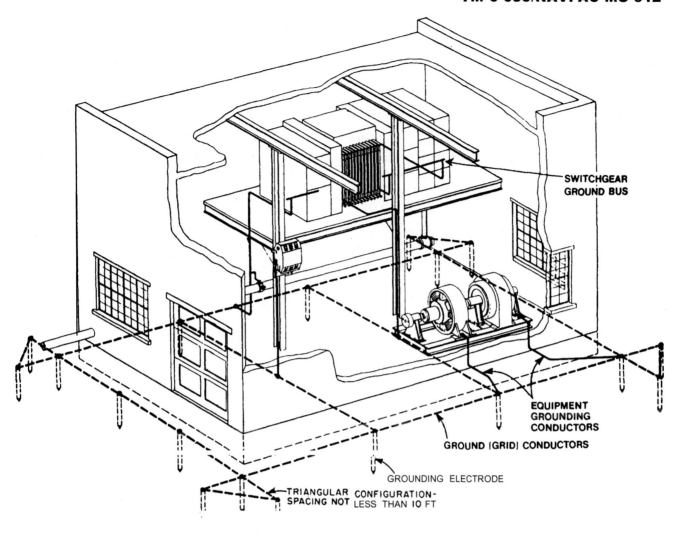

Figure 2-3. Typical grounding system for a building.

flight control). Emergency situations include the handling of priority loads during power "brownouts" and sharing load responsibilities with prime power sources during "brown-outs". Usually load shedding consists of a documented plan that includes a method for reducing or dropping power to noncritical equipment. This plan should include an updated schematic for load shedding reference and "Truth Table" to ensure correct sequencing of dropping and restoring loads on the system. Plans for load shedding are part of the emergency operating instructions and vary from one facility to another. The extent of load shedding and the sequence of dropping loads and restoring to normal are also contained in the plan.

2-10. Components.

Standards for selection of components for an auxiliary power plant are usually based on the electrical loads to be supplied, their demand, consumption, voltage, phase, and frequency requirements. Also to be considered are load trend, expected life of the project and of the equipment, fuel cost and availability, installation cost, and personnel availability and cost. Factors related to prime movers must also be considered: the diesel because of its relatively low cost and good reliability record, as well as its ability to use liquid or gaseous fuel; the gas turbine for permanent standby plants because it is relatively compact in relation to its high generating capacity (desirable if the anticipated power consumption rate is high). The components of the typical power systems are briefly described in the following paragraphs.

a. Prime movers are reciprocating engines, gas turbines, or other sources of mechanical energy used to drive electric generators.

b. Governors control and regulate engine speed. A governor must be capable of regulating engine speed at conditions varying between full-load and no-load and controlling frequency.

c. Generators are machines (rotating units) that convert mechanical energy into electrical energy.

d. Exciters are small supplemental generators that provide DC field current for alternating current generators. Either rotating or static-type exciters are used.

e. Voltage regulators are devices that maintain the terminal voltage of a generator at a predetermined value.

f. Transfer switches are used to transfer a load from one bus or distribution circuit to another, or to isolate or connect a load. The rating of the switch or breaker must have sufficient interrupting capacity for the service.

g. Switchgear is a cabinet enclosure containing devices for electric power control and regulation, and related instrumentation (meters, gauges, and indicator lights).

h. Instrumentation senses, indicates, may record and may control or modulate plant electrical, thermal and mechanical information essential for proper operation. It may also provide an alarm to indicate an unacceptable rate of change, a warning of unsatisfactory condition, and/or automatic shutdown to prevent damage.

CHAPTER 3

PRIME MOVERS

3-1. Mechanical energy.

A prime mover is an engine that converts hydraulic, chemical, or thermal energy to mechanical energy with the output being either straight-line or rotary motion. Rotary mechanical energy is used to drive rotary generators to produce electrical energy. Over the last 125 years, the internal combustion engine, steam turbine and gas turbine have displaced the steam engine. Auxiliary electrical generators are today usually driven by either reciprocating engine or gas turbine. These are available in wide ranges of characteristics and power rating, have relatively high thermal efficiency and can be easily started and brought on line. In addition, their speed can be closely regulated to maintain alternating current system frequency.

a. Fuel is burned directly in the internal combustion engine. The burning air/fuel mixture liberates energy which raises the temperature of the mixture and, in turn, causes a pressure increase. In the reciprocating or piston engine this occurs once for each power stroke. The pressure accelerates the piston and produces work by turning the crankshaft against the connected load.

(1) Reciprocating spark ignition (SI) engines. These engines operate on the Otto Cycle principle typical for all reciprocating SI engines. The events are:

(a) Intake stroke. A combustible fuel/air mixture is drawn into the cylinder.

(b) Compression stroke. The temperature and pressure of the mixture are raised.

(c) *Power (expansion) stroke.* Ignition of the pressurized gases results in combustion, which drives the piston toward the bottom of the cylinder.

(d) Exhaust stroke. The burned gases are forced out of the cylinder.

(2) Four strokes of the piston per cycle are required (four-stroke cycle or four-cycle). One power stroke occurs in two revolutions of the crankshaft.

(3) The output o fan engine can be increased with some loss in efficiency by using a two-stroke (two-cycle) Otto process. During the compression stroke, the fuel/air mixture is drawn into the cylinder. During the power stroke, the mixture in the cylinder is compressed. Near the end of the power stroke, burned gases are allowed to exhaust, and the pressurized new mixture is forced into the cylinder prior to the start of the next compression stroke.

(4) In the Otto cycle, the fuel/air mixture is compressed and ignited by a timed spark. The exact ratio of fuel to air is achieved by carburization of a volatile fuel. Fuel injection is also in use in the Otto cycle to achieve more precise fuel delivery to each cylinder.

(5) Four-cycle SI gasoline engines are used as prime movers for smaller portable generator drives (see fig 3-l). The advantages are:

(a) Low initial cost.

(b) Light weight for given output.

(c) Simple maintenance.

(d) Easy cranking.

(e) Quick starting provided fuel is fresh.

(f) Low noise level.

(6) The disadvantages of using four-cycle SI gasoline engines are:

(a) Greater attendant safety hazards due to use of a volatile fuel.

(b) Greater specific fuel consumption than compression ignition (CI) engines.

(7) Reciprocating CI engines. These operate on the Diesel Cycle principle typical for all CI engines. The-events are:

(a) Intake stroke. Air is drawn into the cylinder.

(b) Compression stroke. Air is compressed, raising the pressure but 'also raising the temperature of the air above the ignition temperature of the fuel to be injected.

(c) *Power stroke.* A metered amount of fuel at greater-than-cylinder-pressure is injected into the cylinder at a controlled rate. The fuel is atomized and combustion occurs, further increasing pressure, thus driving the piston which turns the crankshaft.

(d) Exhaust stroke. The burned gas is forced from the cylinder.

(8) As with the SI four-cycle engine, the four cycles of the CI engine occur during two revolutions of the crankshaft, and one power stroke occurs in every two revolutions.

(9) The CI or diesel engine may also use two cycle operation with increased output but at lower engine efficiency.

(10) In the Diesel cycle, only air is compressed and ignition of the fuel is due to the high temperature of the air. The CI engine must be more stoutly constructed than the SI engine because of the higher pressures. The CI engine requires high-pressure fuel injection.

Figure 3-1. Typical gasoline powered emergency generator set, air cooled.

b. Gas turbine engine. The fuel and air burn in a combustion chamber in the gas turbine engine. The resulting high-pressure gases are directed through nozzles toward the turbine blades and produce work by turning the turbine shaft. This is a continuous process in the continuous-combustion or constant-pressure gas turbine.

(1) Gas turbines operate on the Brayton Cycle principle. While a number of configurations are used for aircraft propulsion (turbofan, turboprop, etc.), the one used as a prime mover for auxiliaries is generally the continuous combustion gas turbine. In this process, air is compressed by an axial flow compressor. A portion of the compressed air is mixed with fuel and ignited in a combustion chamber. The balance of the compressed air passes around the chamber to absorb heat, and then it is merged with the burned products of combustion. The pressurized mixture, usually at 1000°F or higher, flows into a reaction turbine.

(2) The turbine drives the compressor and also produces work by driving the generator. A portion of the exhaust gas may be recirculated and it is possible to recover heat energy from the waste exhaust. The compressor uses a relatively large portion of the thermal energy produced by the combustion. The engine efficiency is highly dependent on the efficiencies of the compressor and turbine.

(3) The advantages of using a gas turbine are:

(a) Proven dependability for sustained operation at rated load.

(b) Can use a variety of liquid and gaseous fuels.

(c) Low vibration level.

(d) High efficiency up to rated load.

(4) The disadvantages of using a gas turbine are:

(a) Initial cost is high.

(b) Fuel and air filtering are required to avoid erosion of nozzles and blades.

(c) Fine tolerance speed reducer between turbine and generator is required and must be kept in alignment.

(d) Specialized maintenance, training, tools and procedures are required.

(e) Considerable energy is required to spin for start.

(f) High frequency noise level.

(g) Exhaust volume is considerable.

(h) A large portion of the fuel heat input is used by the compressor.

(i) A long bedplate is required.

(j) Maximum load is sharply defined.

(h) Efficiency is lower than reciprocating engines.

c. Rotary spark ignition engines. These engines are typified by the Wankel-type engine operating on the Otto principle. Each of the four cycles occurs in a specific sector of an annular space around the axis of the shaft. The piston travels this annular chamber and rotates the shaft. The power stroke occurs once in every shaft revolution, dependent on the design of the engine. This engine can produce a large amount of power for a given size. The high rpm, low efficiency, friction and sealing problems, and unfavorable reliability of this engine make it unsatisfactory as a prime mover for auxiliary generators. These faults may be corrected as the development continues.

3-2. Diesel engines.

Diesel engines for stationary generating units are sized from 7.5 kW to approximately 1500 kW and diesel engines for portable generating units are sized from 7.5 kW to approximately 750 kW. See figures 3-2 through 3-4. Efficiency, weight per horsepower, and engine cost relationships are relatively constant over a wide range of sizes. Smaller engines, which operate in the high-speed range (1200 and 1800 rpm), are used for portable units because of their lighter weight and lower cost. Low- and medium-speed (200 and 900 rpm) engines are preferred for stationary units since their greater weight is not a disadvantage, and lower maintenance cost and longer life offset the higher initial cost.

a. The advantages of diesel engines include:

(1) Proven dependability for sustained operation at rated load.

(2) Efficiency.

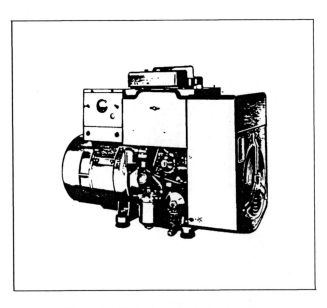

Figure 3-2 Typical small stutionary diesel generator unit, air cooled

(3) Adaptability for wide range of liquid fuels.

(4) Controlled fuel injection.

b. The disadvantages include:

(1) High initial cost.

(2) High weight per given output.

(3) High noise level.

(4) Specialized maintenance.

(5) Fuel injection system has fine mechanical tolerances and requires precise adjustment.

(6) Difficult cranking.

(7) Cold starting requiring auxiliary ignition aids.

(8) Vibration.

3-3. Types of Diesel Engines.

Various configurations of single and multiple diesel engines, either two-cycle or four-cycle are used to drive auxiliary generators. Multi-cylinder engines of either type can be of "V" or in-line configurations.

Figure 3-3. Typical large stationary diesel generator unit.

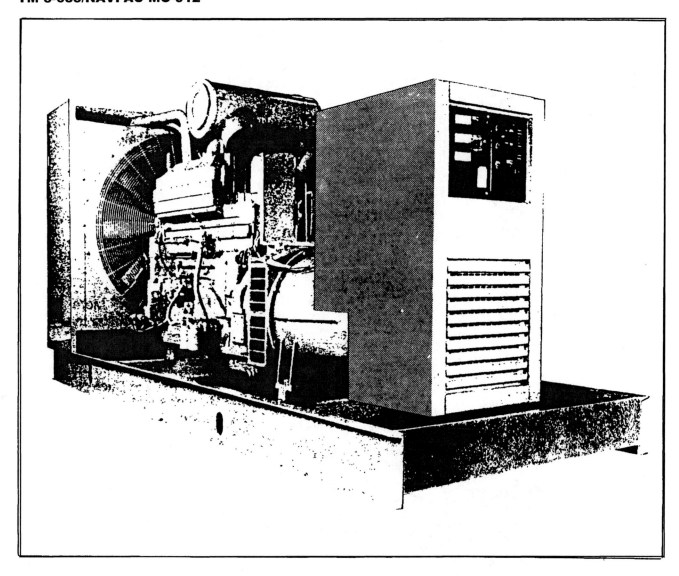

Figure 3-4. Typical diesel power plant on transportable frame base.

The "V" configuration is favored when there is a lack of space because "V" engines are shorter and more compact than in-line engines. Most engines in use are liquid-cooled. Air cooling is sometimes used with single-cylinder and other small engines (driving generators with up to 10 kW output). Air-cooled engines usually reach operating temperature quickly but are relatively noisy during operation.

a. Two cycle. The series of events that take place in a two-cycle diesel engine are: compression, combustion, expansion, exhaust, scavenging, and air intake. Two strokes of the piston during one revolution of the crankshaft complete the cycle.

(1) *Compression.* The cycle begins with the piston in its bottom dead center (BDC) position. The exhaust valve is open permitting burned gases to escape the cylinder, and the scavenging air port is uncovered, permitting new air to sweep into the cylinder. With new air in the cylinder, the piston moves upward. The piston first covers the exhaust

port (or the exhaust valve closes), then the scavenging air port is closed. The piston now compresses the air to heat it to a temperature required for ignition as the piston nears top dead center (TDC). As the piston nears TDC, a metered amount of fuel is injected at a certain rate. Injection atomizes the fuel, which is ignited by the high temperature, and combustion starts. Combustion causes the temperature and pressure to rise further.

(2) *Power:* As the piston reaches and passes TDC, the pressure of the hot gas forces and accelerates the piston downward. This turns the crankshaft against the load connected to the shaft. The fuel/air mixture continues to burn. As the piston passes eighty percent (80%) to eighty-five percent (85%) of the stroke travel towards BDC, it uncovers the exhaust port (or the exhaust valve is opened). This allows exhaust gas to escape from the cylinder. As the piston continues downward, it uncovers the scavenging air port, allowing scavenging air (fresh

air at 3 pounds per square inch (psi) to 6 psi) to sweep the cylinder, further purging the exhaust gas and providing a fresh clean charge for the next cycle. The piston reaches and passes through BDC. The compression stroke then begins again.

b. Four-cycle. The series of events taking place in a four-cycle engine are: inlet stroke, compression stroke, expansion or power stroke, and exhaust stroke. Four strokes (two revolutions of the crankshaft) are necessary to complete the cycle.

(1) *Inlet stroke.* As the piston starts downward from TDC, the inlet (intake) valve opens and allows the piston to suck a charge of fresh air into the cylinder. This air may be supplied at a pressure higher than atmospheric air by a supercharger.

(2) *Compression stroke.* As the piston nears BDC, the air inlet valve closes, sealing the cylinder. Energy supplied by the crankshaft from a flywheel, or power from other cylinders, forces the piston upward toward TDC, rapidly compressing the air and increasing the temperature and pressure within the cylinder.

(3) *Power stroke.* As the piston approaches TDC, an amount of fuel (modulated by the governor) is injected (sprayed and atomized) into the cylinder which is ignited by the high temperature, and combustion starts. Combustion, at a controlled rate, further increases the temperature and pressure to accelerate the piston toward BDC. The expansion of the hot gases forces the piston down and turns the crank against the load. Engine efficiency depends on the fuel charge being completely burned during the power stroke.

(4) *Exhaust stroke.* As the piston passes through BDC at the end of the power stroke, the exhaust valve opens. The piston, using stored energy from the flywheel or from the power stroke of another cylinder, forces the burned gases from the cylinder through the exhaust port. As the piston approaches TDC, the exhaust valve is closed and the air intake valve opens to begin another cycle.

c. Engine timing. Engine timing is critical. Intake and exhaust valves have to open and close to allow the greatest amount of work to be extracted from combustion. They must also be open long enough to allow fresh air to flow into and exhaust gas to flow out of the cylinder. Fuel must be injected at proper rates during certain periods of time to get smooth pressure rise and complete combustion. Timing for two-stroke cycle and four-stroke cycle engines differs (refer to the timing diagrams in fig 3-5). Diagram A illustrates two forms of the two-stroke cycle engine. The inner portion covers the typical crankcase scavenging type with uncontrolled fixed ports.

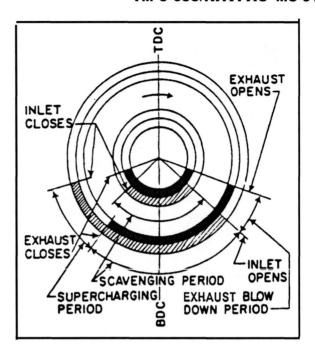

A.

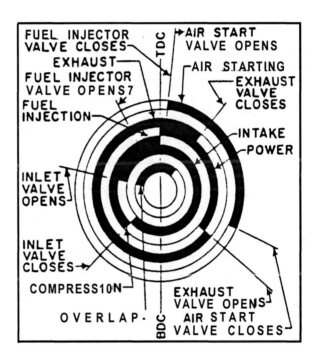

B.

Figure 3-5. Timing diagrams
A) FOR A TWO STROKE CYCLE,
B) FOR A FOUR STROKE CYCLE.

The outer portion covers a port control (uniflow) system. Diagram B illustrates timing for a four-stroke cycle engine.

d. Advantages. Advantages of diesel power for generating units include the ability: to utilize specific liquid or gaseous fuel other than highly volatile refined ones (gasoline, benzene, etc.); to meet load by varying the amount of fuel injected; to utilize a relatively slow design speed; and, to operate without external furnaces, boilers or gas generators.

e. Disadvantages. Major disadvantages include: a need to reduce cranking power by use of compression relief during start and a powerful auxiliary starting engine or starting motor and battery bank; high-pressure, close-tolerance fuel injection systems capable of being finely adjusted and modulated for speed/load control; weight; and, noise.

3-4. Diesel fuel system.

A typical diesel engine fuel system is shown in figure 3-6. Information related to cooling, lubrication, and starting systems is also shown. Functional requirements of a diesel engine fuel system include fuel injection, injection timing, and fuel pressurization.

a. Fuel injection system. This system measures and meters fuel supplied to each cylinder of the engine. Either inlet metering or outlet metering is used. In inlet metering, fuel is measured within the injector pump or injector. In outlet metering, fuel is measured as it leaves the pumping element. Instantaneous rate during injection must deliver fuel to attain correct propagation of the flame front and resulting pressure rise.

b. Timing. Fuel injection timing is critical. The duration of fuel injection and the amount of fuel injected vary during starting and partial, full, or overload conditions, as well as with speed. The best engine start occurs when fuel is injected at (or just before) TDC of piston travel because air in the combustion chamber is hottest at that instant. During engine operation, the injection timing may need to be advanced to compensate for injection lag. Many modern injection systems have an automatic injection timing device that changes timing to match changes in engine speed.

c. Fuel pressurization. Fuel must be pressurized to open the injector nozzle because the nozzle (or injector tip) contains a spring-loaded check valve. The injection pressure must be greater than the compression pressure within the compression chamber or cylinder. Between 1500 psi and 4000 psi pressure is required for injection and proper fuel atomization. Specific information is provided in the engine manufacturer's literature. Fuel system components are listed in paragraph 3-4c.

d. Fuel contamination. Fuel injection equipment is manufactured to precision accuracy and must be very carefully handled. A small amount of abrasive material can seriously damage moving parts. Contaminated fuel is a major vehicle by which dirt and water enter the system. Fuel must be filtered before use.

e. Starting fuels. Diesel engines used for auxiliary generators usually use distillate fuel for quicker starting. These fuels are light oils that are similar to kerosene. Various additives are frequently used with fuel such as cetane improvers which delay ignition for smoother engine operation, corrosion inhibitors, and dispersants. Appendix C contains information related to fuel and fuel storage.

f. Injection systems. Diesel engine manufacturers usually use one of the following types of mechanical fuel injection systems: unit injection, common rail injection, or in-line pump and injection nozzle. A limited number of diesel engines currently in use employ a common rail injection system. Electronic fuel injection has been developed for use in modern diesel engines refer to paragraph 3-4b(4). Unit injector, common rail injector, and in-line pump and injection nozzle systems are described in tables 3-1 through 3-3. Injection of fuel in any system must start and end quickly. Any delay in beginning injection changes the injection timing and causes hard starting and rough operation of the engine. Delay in ending injection is indicated by heavy smoke exhaust and loud, uneven exhaust sounds. The end of injection (full shutoff) should be total with no dribble or secondary injections. Some injection systems include a delivery or retraction valve for fuel shutoff. In other systems, camshafts have cam lobes designed with a sharp drop to assure rapid fuel shutoff.

(1) *Common rail injection.* The common rail injection system is an older system where fuel is supplied to a common rail or manifold. A high-pressure pump maintains a constant pressure in the rail from which individual fuel lines connect to the injection or spray nozzle at each cylinder. Fuel is drawn from the supply tank by the low-pressure pump and passed through a filter to the suction side of the high-pressure pump. The high-pressure pump raises the fuel to the engine manufacturer's specified operating pressure. Constant pressure is maintained in the system by the high pressure pump and related relief valve. If pressure is greater than the relief valve setting, the valve opens and permits some of the fuel to flow back (bypass) into the tank. Check valves in the injection nozzle prevent the return of fuel oil to the injection system by cylinder compression pressure.

(2) *Unit injection.* This system consists of an integral fuel-injector pump and injector unit. A complete unit is required for each cylinder. Fuel oil is

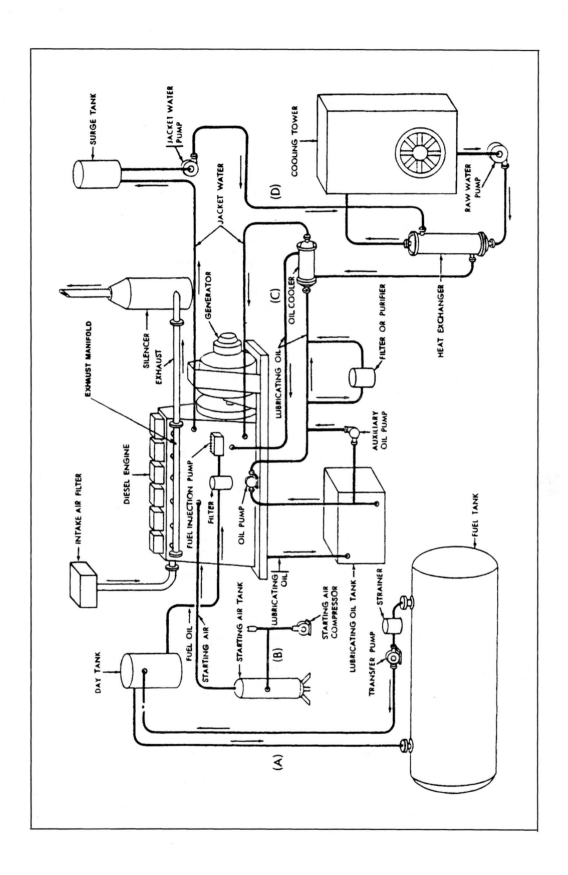

Figure 3-6. Diagram of typical fuel, cooling, lubrication, and starting systems.

Table 3-l. Unit injector system.

Component	Purpose
Gear pump	Low pressure pump; delivers fuel from tank to injector: fuel also lubricates the pump.
Injector	Meters, times, and pressurizes fuel: camshaft-operated by pushrod and rocker arm; one injector for each cylinder.
Filters	Protect machined components from dirt and water in fuel.
Governor	Controls engine speed. Varies position of the injector plunger to vary amount of fuel injected.

Table 3-2. Common rail injector system.

Component	Purpose
Low and high-pressure pump	Low-pressure pump delivers fuel from tank to high-pressure pump; high-pressure pump delivers fuel to injectors at the desired operating pressure: fuel lubricates governor and pumps.
Governor	Flyweight-type; controls maximum fuel pressure; prevents engine overfueling; controls engine idle and prevents overspeeding by controlling fuel supply: contained within main pump housing.
Throttle	Controlled by the operator; regulates fuel flow and pressure to injectors.
Injector	Meters, times and pressurizes fuel; camshaft-operated by pushrod and rocker arm: one injector for each cylinder.
Filters	Protect machined components from dirt and water in fuel.

Table 33. In-line pumps and injection nozzle system.

Component	Purpose
Injection pump	Meters, times, pressurizes and controls fuel delivered to the injection nozzles; consists of single pumping element for each cylinder; titted into a common housing; operated by rocker arm or directly from the camshaft.
Governor	Usually the flyweight-type: may be mounted on main injection pump housing; controls fuel delivery: variable-speed or limiting-speed type is used.
Fuel lines	High-pressure type; transports fuel from pump to injection nozzles.
Injection nozzle	Spring-loaded; hydraulically operated valve that is inserted in the combustion chamber: one nozzle for each cylinder.
Filters	Protect machined components from dirt and water in fuel.

supplied to the cylinders by individual pumps operated from cams located on a camshaft or on an auxiliary drive. The pumps operate independently of each other. Fuel from the supply tank is passed through a filter to the injector pump supply pipe. The injector pump receives the fuel which is then injected into the cylinders in proper quantity and at a prearranged time.

(3) *Electronic Fuel Injection.* The electronic fuel injection system is an advanced design for modern diesel engines, intended to produce improved starting and operating characteristics. Several systems have been developed, mainly for smaller and intermediate-sized engines. Similarities to mechanical injection systems include the following: a fuel pump (or pumps), a governor or speed regulator, filters, and fuel injectors. The major difference between mechanical and electronic systems is the computer which replaces the mechanical components (cams and pushrods) used to control fuel injection. The computer processes data inputs (such as engine speed and load, desired speed or governor setting, engine temperature, and generator load). Computer output is precisely timed electrical signals (or pulses) that open or close the fuel injectors for optimum engine performance. Adjustment of injection timing is seldom required after the initial setup. Refer to the engine manufacturer's literature for maintenance of injectors, pumps, and other fuel system components.

g. The main components of the fuel system. Fuel supply source, transfer pump, day tank, fuel injection pump, fuel injection nozzles, and filters and strainers. These components are matched by the engine manufacturer for optimum performance and warranty protection.

(1) The fuel supply source is one or more storage tanks. Each tank must have drain valves for removal of bottom water, see paragraph 2-4 for general requirements. Additionally, the fuel system should include a day tank and a transfer pump, see paragraph *2-4d.*

(2) The following paragraphs cover the fuel injection pump, fuel injection nozzles, and filters and strainers.

(3) A fuel injection pump accomplishes the functions described in paragraph 3-4b(3). Additional details are provided in the following paragraphs.

(a) The fuel injection pump must perform two functions: first, deliver a charge of fuel to the engine cylinder at the proper time in the engine operating cycle, usually when the piston has almost reached the end of the compression stroke; and second, measure the oil charge delivered to the injector so the amount of fuel is sufficient to develop the power needed to overcome the resistance at the crankshaft.

(b) The fuel injection pump consists of a barrel and a reciprocating plunger. The reciprocating plunger takes a charge of fuel into the barrel and delivers it to the fuel-injecting device at the engine cylinder.

(4) Fuel injection nozzles for mechanical injection systems are usually of the spring-loaded, needle-valve type. These nozzles can be adjusted to open at the predetermined pressure. Consult the manufacturer's specifications before adjusting fuel injection valves. The nozzle components are assembled carefully at the factory and must never be intermixed. Most manufacturers use an individual pump for each cylinder (pump injection system) and provide each cylinder with a spring-loaded spray valve. The spring keeps the needle from lifting until the pump has delivered oil at a pressure greater than the spring loading. As soon as the pressure lifts the needle, oil starts to spray into the engine cylinder through an opening in the valve body.

(5) Diesel fuel suppliers try to provide clean fuel. However, contaminants (water, sand, lint, dirt, etc.) are frequently found even in the best grades. If foreign material enters the fuel system, it will clog the nozzles and cause excessive wear of fuel pumps and injection valves.

(6) Sulphur, frequently found in fuel oil, is very undesirable. When sulfur is burned (during combustion), sulfur dioxide and sulfur trioxide form. Both substances will combine with water condensates to form sulfuric acid. The maximum amount of sulfur acceptable in fuel oil must not exceed one percent. The engine manufacturer's recommendation should be used if acceptable sulfur in fuel oil requirements are more restrictive. Strainers and filters capable of removing fine particles are placed in the fuel line between supply tank and engine, or between engine transfer pump and injection pump, or sometimes at both places. The basic rule for placement of strainers and filters is strainers before pumps, filters after pumps. A filter should be placed in the storage tank fill line. This prevents accumulation of foreign material in the storage tank. Strainers protect the transfer pumps. A strainer should also be placed ahead of each fuel flow meter. Always locate filters and strainers where they are easily accessible for cleaning or replacement. Duplex filters should be provided for engines that run continuously so that filter elements can be cleaned while the engine is running without interrupting its fuel supply. Provide space under the edge of disk filters for a receptacle to receive material drained from the bottom of the filter when it is cleaned. If the filter or strainer has an element that can be renewed or cleaned, space must be allowed to permit its easy removal. Follow the manufacturer's recommendations on frequency of cleaning and replacing filter elements. Adjust the frequency to meet unusual local operating conditions. Generally, all metal-edge and wire-mesh devices are called strainers, and all replaceable absorbent cartridge devices are called filters. Fuel filters approved for military use consist of replaceable elements mounted in a suitable housing. Simplex and duplex type fuel filters are available. Fuel strainers and filters must not contain pressure relief or bypass valves. Such valves provide a means for the fuel to bypass the strainer or filter, thereby permitting the fuel-injection equipment to be damaged by contaminated fuel. Filter capacity is generally described in terms of pressure drop between the input and output sides of the filter. However, fuel oil filters must be large enough to take the full flow of the fuel oil pumps with a pressure drop across the filter not to exceed the engine manufacturer's specifications. Fuel filter elements should be changed whenever the pressure drop across the filter nears or reaches a specified value. Refer to manufacturer's instructions for information on the replacement of filter elements. Filter capacity at a given pressure drop is influenced by the viscosity of the fuel. The filter should have ample capacity to handle fuel demand of the engine at full load. The larger the filter, the less frequently it will have to be cleaned and the better the filtering performance will be.

3-5. Diesel cooling system.

Diesel engines are designed to be either air cooled or liquid cooled. Cooling is used to prevent the cylinder walls, the head, the exhaust manifold, and the lube oil from overheating.

a. An air-cooled system depends on an engine driven fan to blow ambient air over the fluted or finned surfaces of the cylinder head and through a radiator type oil cooler, and over the exhaust manifold. The exterior surfaces must be kept free of dirt or corrosion. The oil must be kept free of sludge to secure adequate cooling. Air cooling is seldom used on engines over 5 HP or on multicylinder engines.

b. The liquid-cooled engine uses a treated coolant forced to circulate through passages in and around the cylinder, head, exhaust manifold and a lube oil heat exchanger. The hot coolant is passed through the tubes of an air-cooled radiator, through the tubes of an evaporative heat exchanger, or through a shell and tube heat exchanger. A typical liquid system is shown in figure 3-7.

(1) Two basic types of liquid-cooling systems are attached and remote.

(a) Attached. All components are mounted at the engine. It is used with smaller and/or portable engine generator sets and usually consists of an engine-driven pump circulating treated coolant in a

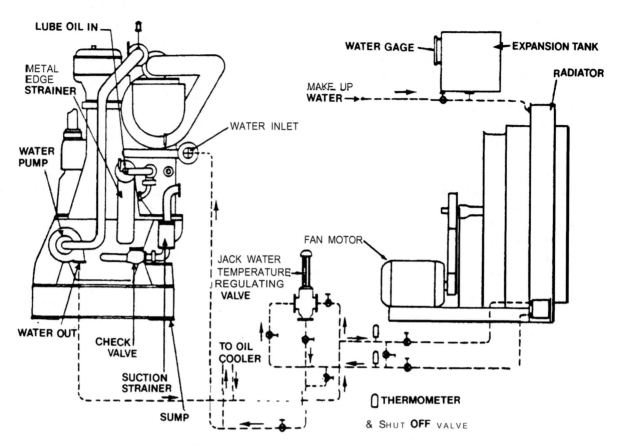

Figure 3-7. Diesel Engine Liquid Cooling System.

closed circuit through a radiator (engine-driven fan) or a water-cooled heat exchanger.

(b) Remote. Primary coolant in a closed circuit is piped to a heat exchanger system not mounted with the engine. Pumps and controls may also be remote. It is used for larger engines where size and complexity of heat dissipation systems are significant. It is also used to physically separate the liquid processing from the electrical generation and control spaces.

c. System description and operation. Successful operation of the engine depends upon the removal of excess heat from lubricating oil, after cooler, and the engine components (cylinders, pistons, and valves) to keep the engine temperature within the limits specified by the manufacturer. The kW rating of the associated electric generator may require derating when any temperature at the operating engine exceeds the manufacturer's limits. Table 3-4 describes the various elements of the cooling system.

(1) Overheating of the engine reduces the effectiveness of engine lubricants, accelerates engine wear, and causes engine breakdown. Cooling prevents excessive stresses in or between engine parts caused by unequal temperature within the engine. Also, cooling prevents loss of strength caused by overheating of the engine's structural metal.

(2) The engine and its components are designed to withstand the mechanical and thermal stresses resulting from operating within certain parameters. The design also allows for the effects of temperature on the strength, resistance to fatigue and wear, the stresses induced by expansion and contraction, and allowance for wear and corrosion, etc.

(a) Each component subject to heat is designed to operate within stated temperature iimits. Unsatisfactory operation, decreased life, damage or failure will result if the engine operates outside of these limits. Lubricants will lose their necessary properties, clearances between parts will become too great or too little, and combustion of fuel will not be proper. Fuel, air, exhaust and coolant passages may be fouled, melted, or chemically attacked, or misalignment and excessive vibrations may result.

(b) Hot spots, cold spots, general overheating and general overcooling can each cause problems. Approximately one-third of the energy consumed by an engine is removed by the cooling system.

(3) An engine used for auxiliary generator service will be one of proven capability and reliability when operated within the limits specified by the manufacturer. A particular engine will require stated rate of coolant flow at certain inlet and outlet temperatures under various rates of fuel energy

Table 3-4. Typical cooling system components.

Component	Purpose
Coolant	The liquid, usually treated water, used to remove excess heat from the engine. May be primary, secondary. etc.
Coolant jackets or passages	Spaces surrounding block, cylinders, and heads, through which primary coolant is circulated under pressure to cool the engine components.
Coolant pumps	Water or primary (secondary, other) pump to circulate coolant (water) through engine passages to heat exchangers.
Thermostat	Regulates coolant flow to maintain engine temperature between specified limits.
Fan	Provides air movement to cool air-cooled engine or the radiator of a liquid-cooled engine to cool the coolant for recirculation.
Shutters	Blades used to vary air flow across a radiator to regulate rate of heat removal from coolant. Would be closed when coolant is below normal temperature and open when coolant is warm. May be thermostatically controlled.
Heat exchanger	A device to exchange heat from one medium to another. Usually a shell and tube-type exchanger.
Coolant tower	A structure in which hot coolant is sprayed or falls through air currents. As coolant evaporates heat is given up by the remaining liquid coolant.
Evaporative cooler	A device to remove heat from medium by evaporation of that medium in air (open circuit). May also be by non-contact heat exchanger from one medium to an evaporating second. Applicable where ambient temperature and relative humidity are below certain values.
Treated coolant	Coolant fluid, usually filtered water with additives to prevent freezing and to inhibit scale formation and corrosion. Required for primary coolant circuit. May not be required for secondary or other circuits.
Secondary system	Describes the components of a second system used to extract heat from the primary heat exchanger. Used where waste heat may be used for building heating, etc.
Tertiary system	Describes components of a possible third system to extract heat from a secondary system.
Closed system	Coolant does not come in contact with air or other fluids.

consumption and mechanical energy output. The coolant must not contain any suspended solids that could settle and impede heat transfer or coolant flow. The coolant should be free of entrained or dissolved air or other gases which could cause corrosion and decrease heat transfer. The coolant should not contain dissolved salts' that could precipitate or form an insulating scale coating which

also decreases heat transfer. It should have good heat capacity and contain an antifreeze, anti-corrosion compound, and cleaning agent to keep coolant passages in good condition. The coolant should neither corrode nor attack any metals or organic materials of the coolant system. It should not be hazardous.

(4) In rare cases, the engine may be cooled using clean water in a once-through system. Cool water is pumped through the coolant passages, and the hot water leaving the engine is discarded. This has many disadvantages and will not be further discussed.

(a) Smaller engines may have a single coolant circuit (loop) through which coolant, leaving the engine, passes and is returned to the engine.

(b) Larger engines may require the use of additional loops. In these, the engine coolant is in a primary loop. It is cooled by the medium circulating in a secondary loop and the secondary coolant may be cooled by another medium in a tertiary loop. No cooling medium mixes with another medium in these "non-contact" systems.

(c) An example of a three-loop system is treated engine coolant in the primary loop passing through a heat exchanger cooled by freshwater in a secondary loop. The "hot" freshwater may be used for building heating or may be passed through another heat exchanger cooled by brackish or saltwater in the tertiary circuit on a once-through basis. The purpose of this arrangement is to keep the seawater at low temperatures so that salts do not form scale. Leakage of seawater into the freshwater circuit is prevented by having the freshwater at higher pressure than the seawater. The freshwater circuit may operate at higher temperature and recover significant usable heat otherwise wasted. Contamination of engine coolant is prevented by being at a higher pressure than the freshwater. The additives used in the engine coolant are a cost. Very little coolant is lost when the coolant circuit is sealed. Heat capacity and temperature may be elevated by using a sealed, pressurized coolant loop. Coolant must be periodically tested to make sure correct amounts of active additives are present.

(d) At the engine the coolant cools the lubricating oil, then the lower temperature areas, and finally the hotter sections.

(e) In the crankcase the oil cools the crankshaft assembly. Sprayed or splashed oil cools the underside of the piston. Oil circulated to the camshaft, rocker arms, and valve guides picks up heat and drains into the sump. The oil pump forces the hot lube oil through the oil filter and through the oil cooler to the pressure-oiled points. The oil must not become so hot that it loses its lubricating properties or breaks down.

(f) Coolant leaving the oil cooler flows to the cylinder water jackets, inlet ports and valves, injectors, exhaust ports and valves, intercooler or supercharger, turboblower, exhaust manifold jacket, and finally to the heat exchanger where it is recirculated to the engine.

(5) Non-contact heat exchangers are used to add or remove heat from one medium to another without intermixing. A radiator or fin-fan cooler uses an airflow to remove and dissipate the heat. In a heat exchanger, one medium flows through tubes and the second medium flows around the tubes. Generally, the medium having a higher tendency to foul the exchanger surfaces is inside the tubes to allow easier cleaning. The tubes may form part of a sealed system. The tube bundle may be in an open tank or in a shell. The shell, enclosing the second medium, may be part of another sealed system.

(6) Cooling towers and evaporative coolers are both used to dissipate waste heat to the atmosphere. They may be used where ambient air is sufficiently cool and dry (low relative humidity) to absorb water vapor. As water is sprayed or divided into many small streams, some will evaporate to the passing air. The heat required to evaporate the water is approximately 1050 Btu/lb and is extracted from the unevaporated water. Additionally, the air which is now moist may be warmed by the water (if the water was originally warmer than the air), thus removing more heat from the water. In a cooling tower, the fluid to be cooled is exposed to the air. Approximately eighty percent (80%) of the heat removed is due to evaporation. The water leaving the tower or cooler is usually five degrees Fahrenheit (5°F) higher than the entering air. Towers may use atmospheric draft or fans to move the air. Makeup water is required to replace that lost by evaporation or entrained spray. Water treatment and blowdown are necessary because salts are concentrated by the evaporation. Dust, etc., in the air will contaminate the exposed water. In an evaporative cooler, the coolant passes through tubes. The tube bundle lies inside a cooling tower. The cooling tower spray and air movement cool the tubes but do not mix with the coolant.

(7) Flow rates of fluid, fan speed, flow bypass, etc. are controlled to maintain proper conditions. A properly monitored, real-time, automatic control system is preferred over a manually-operated system, especially where some parts of the engine auxiliaries are remote or not in direct observation of operating personnel. Automatic data logging is of real value for determining trends and for troubleshooting.

(8) It is necessary to control temperatures at various points of the engine and throughout the cooling systems. This may be done by bypassing some portion of a coolant stream or by changing the flow rate.

(9) Overcooling can cause problems. A warm engine is easier to start and can quickly be brought up to speed and loaded. Warm oil provides better initial oil circulation and lubrication which is vital in cold weather. Heavy fuel oils must be at a temperature related to the viscosity required by the fuel system and injectors. The carburetor and inlet manifold of an SI engine must be warm enough to prevent "icing" and to vaporize the fuel/air mixture. Exhaust gas temperature must be kept above the dew point to prevent condensation and corrosion. An engine running cold will not achieve rated efficiency. Freezing of the coolant can cause breakage or interfere with required flow and circulation.

(10) Chemical control of the various cooling circuits is important. Strainers and filters remove suspended solids. Additives prevent corrosion, mineral scale buildup, organic growth and organic fouling. Periodic sampling and analysis will indicate actual concentrations of undesired materials dissolved in the coolants. Comparison of test results will provide guidance for altering the treatment program. Some untreated freshwater and brackish or seawater promote growth of barnacles, etc., that prevent proper flow and pressures. Visual inspection is recommended when increasing pressure drops indicate fouling. Physical and/or chemical cleaning may be periodically required. Safety precautions must be followed when using most cleaning compounds.

3-6. Lubrication system.

The bearings and moving parts of all diesel engines are lubricated by a full-pressure system, see figure 3-6. Lubricating oil requirements and specifications are covered in appendix C.

a. System elements. Smaller engines are usually self contained. The smaller engine system will have many of the system elements used in the larger engines, as follows:

(1) Lube oil having proper properties for the specific engine design.

(2) Lube oil tank or sump to hold the volume of oil required.

(3) Oil feed pump(s) driven from the engine to circulate clean cool pressurized oil (5 to 75 psi).

(4) Oil feed piping, valves and controls to deliver oil to various lube points of the engine.

(5) Engine internal oil passageways in the crankshaft-piston assembly and in block and head.

(6) Hot oil sump to collect oil draining from all the lubricated engine components.

(7) Hot oil sump pump (return oil pump, filter pump) to force hot used oil through filtering and/or purifier and cooler.

(8) Oil filter to remove suspended solids, dirt and sludge.

(9) Sampling valves for taking samples of oil and filter solids periodically for testing and analysis.

(10) Transfer systems for adding new oil and removing used oil from the engine lube system.

(a) Lube oil must have certain properties for specific application. It must flow properly at the minimum temperatures (pour point), have proper viscosity (resistance to shear) between moving parts and retain desired viscosity over the range of temperatures in the engine (viscosity index). The oil must resist oxidation (stability) that forms gum and sludge and the associated catalytic effects of engine metals present (especially copper and lithium) in the detergent additives. It must allow sludge particles to disperse and not clump or deposit throughout the engine. It will contain inhibitors to prevent oxidation, a dispersing agent and a detergent to keep surfaces clean.

(b) The physical specifications for crankcase lube oil are not positive indications of suitability. The experience of the engine manufacturer is guidance for recommended oils. The user must choose.

(c) Periodic sampling, analysis and evaluation of results is important. An out-of-spec problem will be evident. It is also necessary to look for trends that warn of a condition that may become a major problem. An abnormal rise in the wear metals indicates abnormal wear. Increasing sulphur content and acidity indicates that the lube oil is being contaminated by high-sulfur fuel, oil blowby, etc.

(d) The lube oil tank must be sufficiently large to hold the oil required for the engine. It must be kept clean and closed to prevent contamination of the oil. A vent with flame arrestor should exist. The tank is the reservoir that feeds the oil pumps. The pump suction line should be above any possible sludge or water at the bottom. The tank and all the components of the lube system should be of materials that will not contaminate the oil.

(e) Lube oil pumps circulate the oil at pressure (5 to 75 psi depending on engine design and system pressure losses when cold) through the oil feedline to the engine lube oil header. An auxiliary electrically-driven pump is used prior to starting a cold engine to provide warm oil to all points, especially to heavily loaded main, crank, and wrist pin bearings, to make sure the lubricating film is formed at first movement. This auxiliary pump may also serve as an automatic standby should a normal engine-driven pump system fail. Controls and valv-

ing are provided for that changeover. The auxiliary pump is generally used long enough to return the oil from the critical points and to check the pressure, temperature and flow sensors, indicators, and controls to enable engine cranking. Pumps are usually gear-type with pressure regulation. The engine-driven pump speed is directly related to engine speed so that oil flow increases as speed increases.

b. Types and operation. Large diesel engines use a lubrication system different from that of smaller diesel engines. Because large engines require a large quantity of oil, a separate sump tank is installed to receive oil from the crankcase. The lubricating oil pump draws oil from the sump tank through the strainers. Oil is then discharged, under pressure, into the oil cooler.

(1) The oil then goes to a header, located on the engine, with branches leading to the various parts of the system. Leads extend from the header to each main bearing. After the oil has been supplied to the main bearings, it passes through a drilled passage in the crank web. The oil then passes through a hole in the crank bearing journal to the connecting rod bearing and up through a drilled hole in the connecting rod to the wrist pin. At the wrist pin, the oil, in some engines, passes through a spray nozzle for splash lubrication against the underside of the piston for cooling. The oil then drains down to the engine crankcase and returns to the pump. Other branches from the header rnay supply oil to the gear trains, camshafts and bearings, rocker arms and push rods, cylinder walls, turbo-chargers, blowers, and in some engines, to an oil-cooling system for pistons. Engines may vary in many details, but the principles are the same in all.

(2) Lubricati ng systems of small engines usually are self-contained. The crankcase or a separate oil pan underneath the engine contains all the oil used in the system. Figure 3-8 is a cross section of a diesel engine, showing lube oil flow.

c. Process. The diesel engine lubrication system must circulate, filter, and cool large quantities of lubricating oil. Figure 3-9 shows a schematic arrangement of the main components of a diesel lubrication system. The arrows show the flow of lube oil through the system.

d. Oil storage. All high-speed engines and most medium and low-speed engines use the crankcase base or a sump integral with the crank-case for storing lubricating oil. Several engines operate with a so-called dry crankcase to avoid crankcase oil fog that may cause excessive cylinder lubrication. Such engines must have an outside sump tank placed so that oil from the crankcase will drain into it. One design has an elevated, closed pressure tank to which oil is pumped from the crankcase. Open,

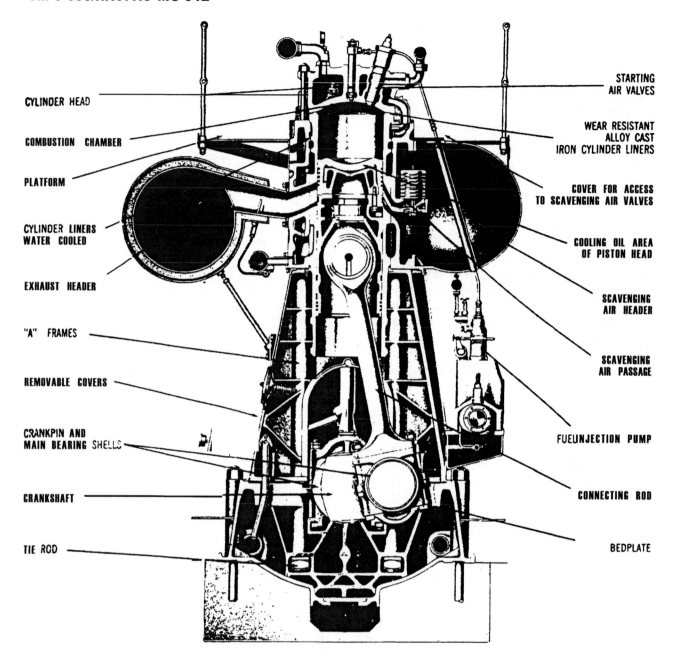

CYLINDER HEAD

COMBUSTION CHAMBER

PLATFORM

CYLINDER LINERS WATER COOLED

EXHAUST HEADER

"A" FRAMES

REMOVABLE COVERS

CRANKPIN AND MAIN BEARING SHELLS

CRANKSHAFT

TIE ROD

STARTING AIR VALVES

WEAR RESISTANT ALLOY CAST IRON CYLINDER LINERS

COVER FOR ACCESS TO SCAVENGING AIR VALVES

COOLING OIL AREA OF PISTON HEAD

SCAVENGING AIR HEADER

SCAVENGING AIR PASSAGE

FUEL INJECTION PUMP

CONNECTING ROD

BEDPLATE

Figure 3-8. Cross Section of a diesel engine showing chamber for lubricating oil collection.

elevated tanks and two sets of pumps are also used. Sump capacities vary with horsepower.

e. Lube oil pumps. In most engines, an engine-driven rotary pump supplies pressure needed to circulate oil through the engine lubrication system. Oil pressure varies from 5 to 60 pounds, depending on diesel engine type. The pressure depends on the amount of clearance in the bearings and the capacity of the pump.

f. Types of pumps. Lubricating oil pumps are usually built into and driven by the engine. In high-speed engines, the oil pump is usually placed in the crankcase sump and driven from the camshaft by a vertical shaft. In larger engines, the pump can be chain-driven by the crankshaft, or mounted at the

end of the engine, either inside or outside the crankcase, and driven by the crankshaft. In other engines, the pump is mounted on the end and driven from the camshaft gears. Larger diesel engines frequently have an auxiliary, motor-driven pump that circulates oil to the bearings before the engine is started. As soon as the engine is up to speed, the pump shuts down. The auxiliary pump also serves as an emergency lubricating oil pump in case the engine-driven pump fails. Finally, the auxiliary pump circulates the oil for a time after the engine is shut down to cool bearings, journals, and pistons. When this method is used, a check valve in the discharge line of the auxiliary pump is necessary to prevent the oil from flowing back when the engine

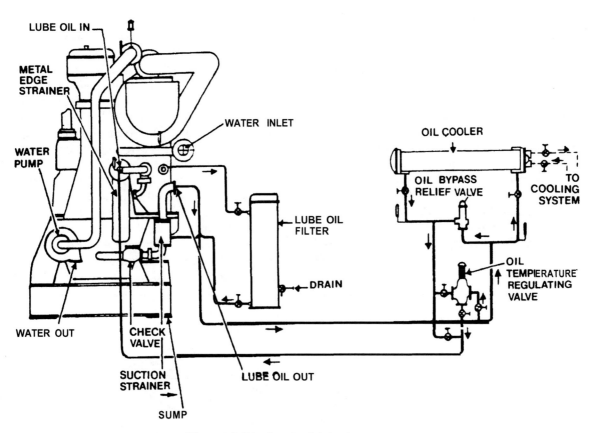

Figure 3-9. Diesel engine lubrication system.

comes up to speed and the auxiliary pump is shut down. The check valve also prevents loss of oil in case of leakage.

g. Heating. Circulating lubricating oil absorbs heat from the engine. Frictional heat is absorbed from the bearings. The oil film on the cylinder walls absorbs heat from the combustion space before this oil film drains into the crankcase. Heat must be dissipated by a cooler if the temperature is to be kept below 230° Fahrenheit. At higher temperatures, oil oxidizes and sludge forms. An oil cooler is necessary when heat dissipated from the oil (by conduction through the walls of the sump and by contact with water-cooled surfaces in the engine) is insufficient to keep the temperature below manufacturer's recommendations. A cooler is particularly necessary for engines having oil-cooled pistons.

h. Coolers. The oil cooler should be placed in the oil circuit after the lubricating oil filter. The filter then handles hot oil of lower viscosity than if it received cooled oil. The filter performance is better and the pressure drop through it is less with this arrangement. Coolers are usually mounted on the side of the engine or on the floor alongside of the engine base. Cooling water passes through the cooler before entering the engine jackets. Exceptions, such as placing the oil-cooling coils in the water jackets at one end of the engine, are permis-

sible. Also, the coils may be placed in the side jackets. Some designs have the coil tubes in the cooling water header, while in others, water entering the cooler is bypassed around the jacket system.

i. Oil filters. Proper installation and maintenance of oil filters and mechanical operation of the engine are equally important for treatment of oil. Prevention of contamination and removal of contaminants should be coordinated. Because high-detergent oils are used in engines, the purification system should not remove the additive. Cellulose filter cartridges do not remove the additive, but a fuller's earth filter does. In large engine installations, a centrifuge may be used with filter purifiers, or large continuous oil purifiers may be used in lieu of the centrifuge. Centrifuging does not remove acids because acidic compounds have approximately the same specific gravity as oil. Batch settling effectively removes organic acids from oil, improving its neutralization number. When purifiers are used, they should be used in addition to, not in place of, lube oil filters.

3-7. Starting system.

The starting system for diesel engines described in this manual must perform as follows for automatic start-up when primary electric power fails: compress the air in the combustion chambers and deliver fuel for combustion. To do this, the starting system must rotate (crank) the engine at a speed sufficient to raise the cylinder air charge to the fuel igniting temperature. See figure 3-6.

a. *Types.* Two types of starting systems are available for the required automatic start-up capability: electric starting and air starting.

(1) Electric *starting.* Most small diesel engines use an electric starting system. This type of system is generally similar to a starter for an automotive gasoline engine. Smaller diesel engines use a 12-volt battery-powered system for cranking. Starter and battery systems of 24, 32, and 48 volts are often used for larger engines. A typical system consists of storage batteries (as required for voltage output) connected in series, a battery charging system, and the necessary grounding and connecting cables. See figure 3-10.

(2) *Air starting.* Some larger engines may use an air starting system. Compressed air at a pressure of 250 or 300 psi is delivered to the working cylinder's combustion chambers during the power stroke. This action results in positive and fast rotation (cranking). Depending on the manufacturer's design, compressed air can be delivered to all or selected cylinders. This type of system requires an air compressor and receivers or air bottles for storage of compressed air.

(3) *Air starter motor.* Pneumatic air starter motors are highly reliable. Air starter motors develop enough torque to spin the engine at twice the cranking speed in half the time required by electric starter motors. Compressed air at a pressure of 110 to 250 psi is stored in storage tanks, regulated to 110 psi and piped to the air motor. A check valve

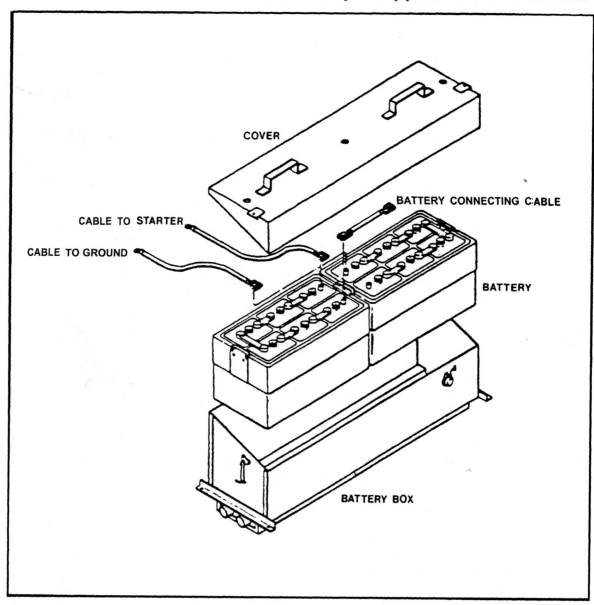

Figure 3-10. Battery for engine starting system.

installed between the compressor and the storage tanks will prevent depletion of compressed air should the plant system fail. Air starter motors are suitable on diesel engine driven generators ranging from 85 kW up to the largest diesel engine generator.

3-8. Governor/speed control.

A diesel engine used in an auxiliary generator must have a governor to regulate and control engine speed. Since an automatic governor functions only with a change in speed, constant engine speed may not be totally possible and "hunting" can occur due to over-correction. The governor's sensitivity is determined by the minimum change in speed of the prime mover which will cause a change in governor setting; its speed regulation is the difference in generator speeds at full-load and no-load divided by the arithmetical mean of the two speeds. Refer to the glossary for descriptions of governor characteristics.

a. Usually, this ratio is stated as a percentage, with synchronous speed considered rather than mean speed. For example, a generator with a synchronous speed of 1,200 rpm, operated at 1,190 rpm when fully loaded and 1,220 rpm with no load, has 2.5 percent speed regulation.

b. The governor must be capable of speed adjustment so the proper governed speed can be selected. In most governors, this adjustment is made by changing the tension of the main governor spring. The governor should also be adjustable for speed regulation so the droop of the speed-load curve can be altered as required to suit operating conditions. Determine the curve by observing the generator speed or frequency at various loads and plotting them as abscissa against the loads (from no-load to full-load) as ordinates. The curve droops at the full-load end (hence, the expression "speed droop" of the governor).

c. An example of speed droop characteristics is shown in figure 3-11. The characteristics are for a mechanical governor but the same principles can be used for other engine/governor applications. The chart is based on a six percent speed droop governor on an engine running at rated speed at no load. When full load is applied, engine speed drops to 94 percent (94%) of rated value (line B). The engine can be brought to rated speed at full load by resetting the governor (line A). However, with the load removed, engine speed would increase beyond its rated limit. Intermediate speed settings are shown by lines C and D. Line E shows speed droop at 50 percent (50%) load.

d. Speed droop can be determined quickly by loading the generator to full-load, observing the speed, unloading the generator, and again observing

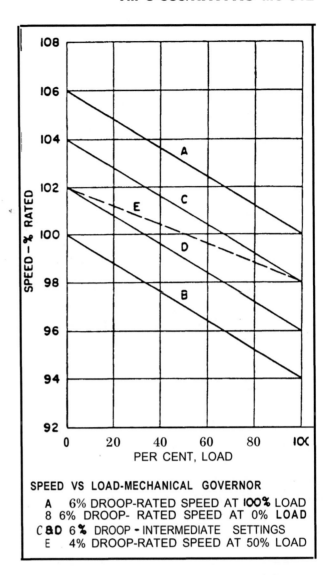

Figure 3-11. Chart of speed droop characteristics.

the speed. Speed droop is usually adjusted by lengthening or shortening the governor operating levers, changing the ratio between governor movement and throttle or gate movement.

e. Alternating Current (AC) Generators. Governors of prime movers driving AC generators which operate in parallel with other generators must have enough speed regulation or speed droop to prevent surging of the load from one generator to another. Ordinarily, three to five percent speed regulation is adequate. Some governors have antisurging devices to damp out the surges. Speed regulation should be increased if the surges continue. Speed regulation of governors controlling AC generators affects the frequency and the load division between generators but has almost no effect upon voltage.

f. Direct Current (DC) Generators. Regulation of DC generators affects voltage regulation and the division of load between generators. In general, the speed regulation of generators operated in parallel should be the same for each machine. Speed regulation for generators operating individually should be as favorable as possible without causing generator surge resulting from sudden load changes. Ordinarily, 2.5 percent speed regulation is satisfactory Voltage regulation of DC generators may be accomplished through adjustment of the speed droop of the governor.

g. Types of governors. Usually four types of governors are used; mechanical, hydraulic, pneumatic, and electronic. When speed regulation must be more precise, such as Defense Communications Agency sites where no more than 0.8 percent variation is permitted, an electronic (isochronous) governor is used.

(1) The mechanical governor used in small air-cooled engines may be part of the fly-wheel. The governor in multicylinder engines is usually a separate assembly driven by gear or belt from a camshaft or crankshaft. A typical mechanical governor, shown in figure 3-12, operates as follows: the governor drive gear (2) drives the governor shaft (10) and the governor weights (4). Centrifugal force moves the weights away from the shaft which push the operating-fork riser (6) against the operating fork (11), rotating the operating-fork shaft (7) and moving the governor arm (9). In the external view, the governor spring (A) is connected to the governor arm and opposes movement of the governor weights away from the shaft. Adjusting screw (c) adjusts the tension of the governor spring, establishing the speed at which the prime mover operates. The greater the governor-spring tension, the lower the governed speed. The auxiliary adjusting screw (D) adjusts the droop of the governor. Turning this screw in closer to the arm decreases the droop of the governor; this screw should be turned in as far as possible without allowing the engine to surge. Auxiliary adjusting screw (B) is turned in to damp out surging of the engine at light-load or no-load; it should not be turned in so far that it increases the speed of the generator at no-load.

(2) The hydraulic governor (see fig 3-13) is used on large prime movers as well as diesel engines as small as 100 hp. The governor usually includes: a speed-responsive device, usually flyweights; a valve mechanism; a regulating cylinder and piston; and a pressure pump and relief valve. The assembly is adjustable for various ranges of speed and sensitivity. The hydraulic principle provides greater power than could be obtained from a mechanical type. Since the flyweights only control an easily moved pilot valve (which in turn controls the hydraulic action), the governor can be made to operate accurately and smoothly. Remote control

and automatic equipment can be applied to the hydraulic governor.

(a) The hydraulic governor requires pressurized oil for operation. This oil can come from the engine or from a separate sump in the governor. Oil is admitted to an auxiliary oil pump in the governor. The auxiliary pump furnishes necessary pressure to actuate the governor mechanism. In the governor shown, the fuel to the engine is decreased by the action of the fuel-rod spring (10) on the fuel rod (12) and increased by the opposing action of the hydraulic serve piston (14), the admission of oil to which is controlled by a pilot valve (4). The pilot valve is controlled by flyweights of the governor (5) which are driven by the governor shaft through gearing to the engine. The centrifugal force of the flyweights in rotation is opposed by the speeder spring (6), the compression of which determines the speed at which the governor will control the engine. The speeder-spring compression is adjusted through the rotation of the speed-adjusting shaft (8) which raises or depresses the spring fork (7) through its linkage lever.

(b) The droop of the speed-load characteristic is adjusted by changing the effective length of the floating lever (11). This is accomplished by moving the droop-adjusting bracket forward or backward in the slot of the floating lever. The effective length of the lever should be shortened to decrease the speed droop and lengthened to increase the speed droop.

(3) The pneumatic governor (air-vane type) is used in certain small generator plants (see fig 3-14). The engine flywheel includes an integral fan which forces air outward from the drive shaft. The amount of air flowing from the engine depends on engine speed. A movable air vane is placed in the air stream. The air vane (blade) acts as a governor since the air pressure depends upon engine speed. The air pressure on the vane is opposed by a governor spring and these forces operate through linkage to control the throttle of the engine.

(4) Electronic (isochronous) speed control is the maintenance of constant engine speed independent of the load being carried (zero droop). An isochronous governor will maintain, or can be adjusted to maintain, constant engine speed (within 0.2 percent variation). This type of governor can be a combination of a conventional hydraulic governor and an electronic load-sensing system, or an all-electric system.

(a) Speed control by the hydraulic governor, see paragraph 3-8d(2), depends on variation in centrifugal force created by flyweights (centrifugal forces are not used in electric types). This force operates a piston-type pilot valve which controls the

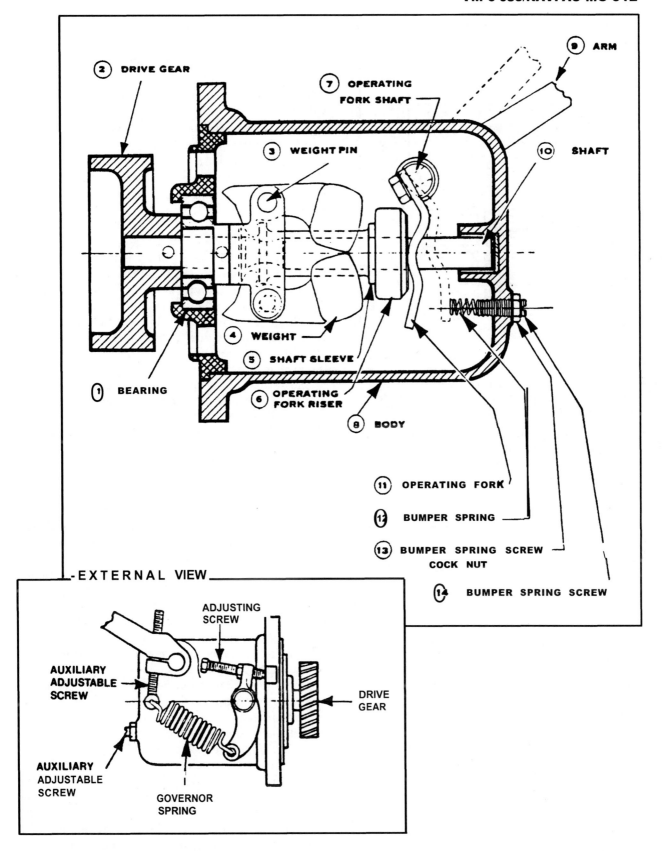

Figure 3-12. Mechanical Governor.

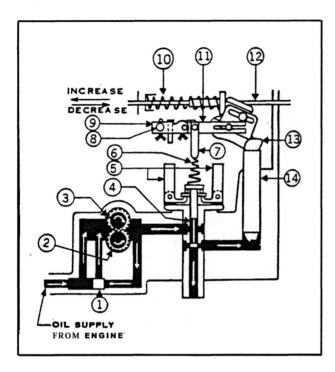

Figure 3-13. Hydraulic Governor.
1) PLUNGER, 2) GEAR PUMP DRIVE, 3) GEAR PUMP
IDLER, 4) PLUNGER PILOT VALVE, 5) FLYWEIGHT,
6) SPEEDER SPRING, 7) SPRING FORK,
8) SPEED-ADJUSTING SHAFT, 9) SPEED-ADJUSTING
LEVER, 10) SPRING, 11) FLOATING LEVER,
12) FUEL ROD, 13) TERMINAL LEVER,
14) SERVO PISTON

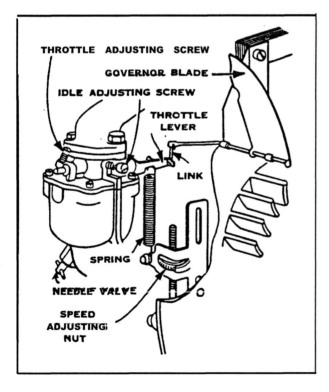

Figure 3-14. Carburetor and pneumatic governor.

flow of high-pressure oil to a servomotor, thereby operating fuel controls.

(b) The isochronous system uses electronic sensing and amplifying devices that actuate a type of servomotor throttle control. The system is used with power generation where precise frequency control is required. An isochronous system may be sensitive to frequency changes (engine speed) or to both frequency and load. When responsive to load changes, the system corrects fuel settings before load changes can appreciably modify engine speed or frequency.

3-9. Air intake system.

Approximately 15 pounds of air is required to burn one pound of fuel. Accordingly, the air requirement for a 2000 horsepower engine is about 3600 cubic feet per minute. The same horsepower-to-air relationship applies to engines for other power ratings. Intake air carries dust particles, water vapor and other foreign material. Since these materials can damage moving parts within the engine, filtration of the intake air is necessary. A 2000 horsepower engine, breathing air containing three parts per million dust contamination, would take in 25 pounds of foreign material in 1000 operating hours. An air intake system must collect, filter, and distribute the required air to the engine cylinders. This must be accomplished with a minimum expenditure of energy (pressure drop). The objective of air filtration is the reduction of engine component wear. Several types of air filters or air cleaners are used. The pleated-paper type are strainers, porous enough to pass air but able to remove solid particles larger than 0.002 of an inch. Larger engines use an oil-bath air cleaner (see fig 3-15). In oil-bath cleaners air is drawn through an oil bath. Solid particles are trapped and settle in the unit's bottom pan.

a. Supercharging. Supercharging increases the amount of air taken into a working cylinder. This provides the injected fuel oil with more oxygen to enable combustion of a larger charge of air/fuel mixture. Power output of a certain size engine is thereby increased, enabling use of smaller engines where space prohibits larger engines.

(1) Advantages. The power output of a naturally aspirated engine is limited by the normal pressure and oxygen content of the atmosphere. When supercharging is used, the intake valve (port) closes with the cylinder under the initial pressure. Supercharging is particularly effective at higher altitudes. The supercharged engine can develop greater horsepower than the standard naturally-aspirated unit. The fuel consumption of a supercharged unit will not exceed that of comparable horsepower sizes of naturally-aspirated units.

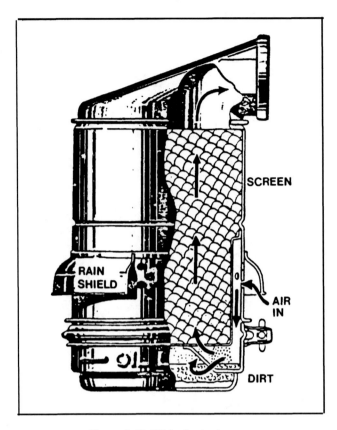

Figure 3-15. Oil bath air cleaner:

(2) *Methods.* The most successful method of supercharging is the use of a turbocharger driven by exhaust gas (see fig 3-16). The heat and energy pulsations in the exhaust gas, which are usually lost in the exhaust silencer, are used to drive a single-stage centrifugal turbine. The exhaust gas turbine is coupled to a centrifugal compressor that compresses the air to a pressure of four or five psi. The engine's pressurized air is then delivered to the individual cylinders through the intake manifold.

(3) *Disadvantages.* Although the supercharged engine has many advantages over nonsupercharged engines, its disadvantages are not insignificant. The turbocharger is another piece of equipment to maintain and operate. It operates at varying speeds depending on engine load, barometric pressure, inlet air temperature, exhaust temperature, smoke content of the exhaust, or accumulations of dust and dirt on the impeller and diffuser. It may operate at very high speed (up to 120,000 rpm) with a full load on the engine and thus be subjected to all the troubles of high-speed equipment. With proper maintenance, however, the turbocharger can be operated very successfully. If the turbocharger fails, the engine can usually be operated at reduced load as a nonsupercharged engine. The turbocharger can be partially dissembled and the opening blocked off,

but the coolant should be allowed to circulate through the supercharger.

(4) *Operating instructions.* Manufacturer's instructions must be followed to ensure proper operation of superchargers. Filtered air only should enter the air inlet, because foreign matter can cause rotor imbalance and damaging vibration. The manufacturer's recommendations for lubrication must be followed. Proper lubrication is necessary because the unit operates at high speed and at high temperature. Not more than 15 seconds should elapse between the start of rotation and an oil pressure indication of 12 to 71 psi. Coolant circulation through the turbocharger should be regulated so the temperature rise does not exceed 30" Fahrenheit at full engine load. A rise in excess of 30" Fahrenheit indicates faulty circulation. Coolant should be allowed to circulate through the turbocharger for about 5 minutes after the engine is shutdown.

b. Aspiration. The term "naturally-aspirated" is applied to engines that are not supercharged. A four stroke cycle engine performs its own air pumping action with the piston intake stroke. When it is supercharged, a four-stroke engine with a blower or turbocharger provides pressure in the intake manifold greater than atmospheric. The increased pressure in the intake manifold is referred to as "boost". Two stroke cycle engines require an air supply under pressure to provide scavenging air.

3-10. Exhaust system.

Components. The exhaust system consists of the engine exhaust manifold and includes piping, expansion joints, silencers, and exhaust pipe. Also the system may include exhaust waste heat recovery equipment. The purpose of the system is to remove exhaust gas from engine cylinders to the atmosphere. Parts of the system are shown in figure 3-6.

(a) Leak-free. Exhaust systems must be leak free to protect personnel from asphyxiation, and equipment from fire and explosion. Exhaust from gasoline engines can contain dangerous carbon monoxide. Diesel engine exhaust includes objectionable smoke and odors. On supercharged engines, leaks ahead of the turbine cause a loss of power.

(b) Piping. Exhaust piping must be the correct size to minimize exhaust back pressure. Connections between exhaust manifold and piping should have an expansion joint and the exhaust pipes should slope away from the engine. Also the exhaust pipes should have suitable devices to prevent entry of rainwater. The length of tail pipes from silencer to atmosphere should be kept to a minimum.

(c) Silencers. Silencers are used to reduce or muffle engine exhaust noise. Silencing engine exhaust sounds consists of trapping and breaking up

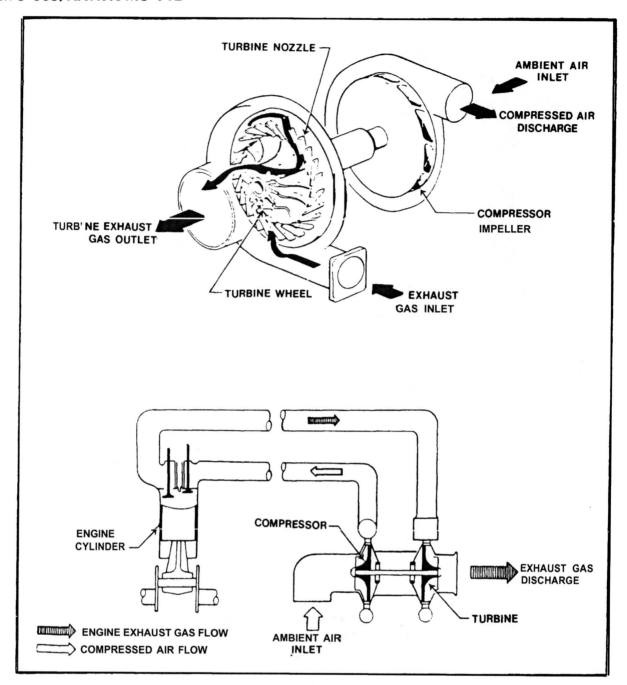

Figure 3-16. Diagram of turbocharger operation.

the pressure waves. Usually, a cylindrical unit with baffles, expansion chambers, and sound absorption materials is used.

3-11. Service practices.

a. Maintenance program. Service practices for diesel engines consist of a complete maintenance program that is built around records and observations. The maintenance program includes appropriate analysis of these records. DD Form 2744 (Emergency/Auxiliary Generator Operation Log) should be used to record inspection testing of emergency/auxiliary generators. A copy of DD Form

2744 is provided at the back of this publication. A completed example of DD Form 2744 is located in appendix F, figure F-l. It is authorized for electronic generation.

(1) Record keeping. Engine log sheets are an important part of record keeping. The sheets must be developed to suit individual applications (i.e., auxiliary use) and related instrumentation. Accurate records are essential to good operations. Notes should be made of all events that are or appear to be outside of normal range. Detailed reports should be logged. Worn or failed parts should be tagged and protectively stored for possible future reference and

analysis of failure. This is especially important when specific failures become repetitive over a period of time which may be years.

(2) *Log sheet data.* Log sheets should include engine starts and stops, fuel and lubrication oil consumption, and a cumulative record of the following:

(a) Hours since last oil change.

(b) Hours since last overhaul.

(c) Total hours on engine.

(d) Selected temperatures and pressures.

b. *Troubleshooting.* Perform troubleshooting procedures when abnormal operation of the equipment is observed. Maintenance personnel should then refer to log sheets for interpretation and comparison of performance data. Comparisons of operation should be made under similar conditions of load and ambient temperature. The general scheme for troubleshooting is outlined in the following paragraphs.

(1) *Industrial practices.* Use recognized industrial practices as the general guide for engine servicing. Service information is provided in the manufacturer's literature and appendixes B through G.

(2) *Reference Literature.* The engine user must refer to manufacturer's literature for specific information on individual units. For example, refer to table 3-5 for troubleshooting an engine that has developed a problem.

Table 3-5. Diesel engines troubleshooting.

HARD STARTING OR FAILS TO START

Cause	Remedy
Air intake restricted.	Check intake and correct as required.
Fuel shut-off closed, low supply of fuel.	Make sure shut-off is open and supply is at proper level.
Poor quality fuel.	Replenish fuel supply with fresh, proper quality fuel.
Clogged injector.	Clean all injectors, refer to appendix G.
Injector inlet or drain connection loose. Engine due for overhaul.	Check all connections and correct as required. Schedule the overhaul and correct as required.
Incorrect timing.	Perform timing procedure, refer to appendix G.

ENGINE MISSES DURING OPERATION

Air leaks in fuel suction lines.	Check fuel suction lines and correct as required.
Restricted fuel lines.	Check fuel lines and correct as required.
Leakage at engine valves.	Refer to manufacturer's instructions and correct as required.
Incorrect timing.	Perform timing procedure, refer to Appendix G.

EXCESSIVE SMOKING AT IDLE

Restricted fuel lines.	Check fuel lines and correct as required.

Table 3-5. Diesel engines troubleshooting-Continued

EXCESSIVE SMOKING AT IDLE

Cause	Remedy
Clogged injector. Leaking head gasket or blowby. Engine due for overhaul. Incorrect timing.	Clean all injectors, refer to appendix G. Refer to manufacturer's instruction and correct as required. Schedule the overhaul and correct as required. Perform timing procedures. refer to appendix G.

EXCESSIVE SMOKING UNDER LOAD

The same causes for "idle" apply.	The same remedies for "idle" apply.
Air intake restricted.	Check air intake and correct as required.
High exhaust back pressure.	Check exhaust system and turbocharger; correct as required.
Poor quality fuel.	Replenish fuel supply with fresh, proper quality fuel.
Engine overloaded.	Reduce load to proper ievel.

LOW POWER OR LOSS OF POWER

Air intake restricted.	Check air intake and correct as required.
Poor quality fuel.	Replenish fuel supply with fresh, proper quality fuel.
Clogged injector.	Clean all injectors, refer to appendix G.
Faulty throttle linkage or governor setting too low.	Check linkage and governor refer to manufacturer's instructions and correct as required.
Clogged filters and screens.	Clean filters and screens.
Engine overloaded.	Reduce load to proper level.
Engine due for overhaul.	Schedule the overhaul and correct as required.
Incorrect timing. Engine requires tune-up.	Perform timing procedure, refer to appendix G. Perform tune-up procedure, refer to appendix G.

DOES NOT REACH GOVERNED SPEED

The same causes for "low power", apply.	The same remedies for "low power", apply.

EXCESSIVE FUEL CONSUMPTION

Air intake restricted.	Check air intake and correct as required.
High exhaust back pressure.	Check exhaust system and turbocharger; correct as required.
Poor quality fuel.	Replenish fuel supply with fresh. proper quality fuel.
Faulty injector.	Clean all injectors, refer to appendix G.
Engine overloaded.	Reduce load to proper level.
Engine **due** for overhaul.	Schedule the overhaul and correct as required.
Incorrect timing.	Perform timing procedure, refer to appendix G.

ENGINE QUITS

Air intake restricted.	Check air intake and correct as required.

Table 3-5. Diesel engines troubleshooting---Continued

ENGINE QUITS

Cause	Remedy
High exhaust back pressure turbocharger.	Check exhaust system and correct as required.
Fuel shut-off closed, low supply of fuel.	Make sure shut-off is open and supply is at proper level.
Poor quality fuel.	Replenish fuel supply with fresh, proper quality fuel.
Faulty injector.	Clean all injectors, refer to appendix G.

ENGINE SURGES AT GOVERNED SPEED

Cause	Remedy
Air leaks in fuel suction lines.	Check fuel suction lines and correct as required.
Faulty injector.	Clean all injectors, refer to appendix G.
Leaks in oil system.	Check for oil leaks, check oil lines, check crankcase drain plug and gasket; correct as required.
Engine due for overhaul.	Schedule the overhaul and correct as required. Piston rings or cylinder liners may be worn.

SLUDGE IN CRANKCASE

Cause	Remedy
Fouled lubricating oil strainer or filter.	Check strainers and filters, remove and service as required, reinstall on engine with new gaskets.
Faulty thermostat.	Check coolant thermostats, engine may be too cool.
Dirty lubricating oil.	Drain old oil, service strainers and filters, refill with fresh oil.

LUBRICATING OIL DILUTED

Cause	Remedy
Fuel in lubricating oil.	Check for loose injector inlet or drain connection; correct as required. Drain old oil, service strainers and filters, refill with fresh oil.
Coolant in lubricating oil.	Check for internal coolant leaks. Correct as required. Drain old oil, service strainers and filters, refill with fresh oil.

LOW LUBRICATING OIL PRESSURE

Cause	Remedy
Faulty oil line, suction line restricted, low oil level.	Check oil lines for good condition, fill to proper oil level with fresh oil.
Engine due for overhaul.	Schedule the overhaul and correct as required. Piston rings, crankshaft bearings, or cylinder liners may be worn.

ENGINE RUNNING TOO HOT

Cause	Remedy
High exhaust back pressure.	Check exhaust system and turbocharger; correct as required.
Faulty thermostat.	Check coolant thermostats; correct as required.
Low lubricating oil level.	Fill to proper level with fresh oil.
Engine overload.	Reduce load to proper level.
Faulty cooling system component (pump, hose, radiator fan belt).	Check components; correct as required. Fill cooling system to proper level with coolant.

Table 3-5. Diesel engines troubleshooting-Continued

ENGINE RUNNING TOO HOT

Cause	Remedy
Low coolant level. Air in system.	Refer to appendix D.

ENGINE KNOCKS

Cause	Remedy
Poor quality fuel.	Replenish fuel supply with fresh, proper quality fuel.
Air leaks in fuel suction lines.	Check fuel suction lines and correct as required.
Engine overloaded.	Reduce load to proper level.
Engine running too hot.	Repeat the procedures for "too hot", above.
Faulty vibration damper or flywheel.	Correct as required, refer to manufacturer's instructions.
Engine due for overhaul.	Schedule the overhaul and correct as required.

3-12. Operational trends and engine overhaul.

a. Trending data. Usually, a graphic presentation of data simplifies detection of a trend toward deteriorating engine performance. Samples of graphic aids are shown in figures 3-17 and 3-18. These include plots of fuel and lubricating oil consumption versus electric load (power production), monthly pressure checks (engine parameters), and maintenance data showing cylinder wear and crankshaft deflection. Interpretation of data and details are provided in the specific engine manufacturer's literature. These kinds of data aid in developing criteria for equipment performance and determining the need for engine overhaul or other repair.

(1) Samples of information appearing in figure 3-17 are as follows:

(a) "A" on the chart may indicate lack of operating hours.

(b) "B" on the chart may indicate a peak value or seasonal characteristic.

(c) "C" on the chart may indicate the result of frequent starts or stops. "D" on the chart indicates a steady improvement.

(d) "E" on the chart shows lubricating oil consumption. The steady decline at "F" may indicate a developing engine problem (i.e., oil control ring failure, lube oil leakage into combustion areas, or excessive oil feed).

(2) Samples of information appearing in part A of figure 3-18 are as follows:

(a) "A" on the chart may indicate faulty fuel injectors, or deviations in fuel timing.

(b) "B" on the chart (sharp rise in compression) can be caused by carbon build up or may indicate new piston rings were installed.

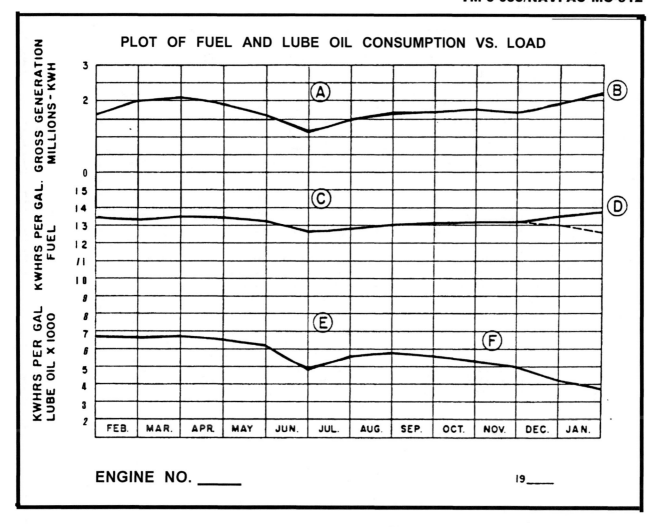

Figure 3-17. Performance data plots.

(c) "C" on the chart may indicate a developing engine problem.

(d) "D" on the chart indicates engine governor positions relative to "A", "B", and "C".

b. *Engine overhaul.* An engine consists of structural parts and moving parts. Structural parts are those having no movement relative to each other. They do not involve clearances, adjustments, or lubrication. These parts consist of the following: foundation, bedplate, foundation bolts, frames, cylinders and block, cylinder heads, covers and associated gaskets, and auxiliary housings. Moving parts are those that normally require fitting and/or clearance adjustment. These parts consist of the following: crankshaft (including journal surfaces, counterweights, gears, and flywheels), main bearings, thrust bearings, camshafts and bearings, connecting rods and bearings, pistons (including rings and pins), timing gear mechanisms, and auxiliary or accessory drives. All of these parts are engineered and designed by the engine manufacturer to perform a particular task. When the need to overhaul an engine is indicated by operational malfunctions

(refer to the troubleshooting table) consult the specific manufacturer's literature for instructions.

c. *Overhaul procedure.* Engine overhaul requires disassembly of the engine. Verify that all engine parts comply with the manufacturer's specifications and tolerances.

(1) Inspect structural parts as follows:

(a) Foundations for deformation and cracks.

(b) Bedplate for cracks and distortion; bearing supports for good condition.

(c) Foundation bolts for tightness and general good condition including straightness.

(d) Frames for cracks, distortion, and general good condition.

(e) Cylinders and cylinder blocks for cracks; water jacket areas for corrosion, scale, and rust; machined surfaces for smoothness.

(f) Cylinder heads for cracks; water jacket areas for corrosion, scale, and rust; valve seats for cracks; machined surfaces for smoothness.

(g) Covers and gaskets for distortion and cracks; use satisfactory gaskets only after annealing; use new seals and gaskets other than copper.

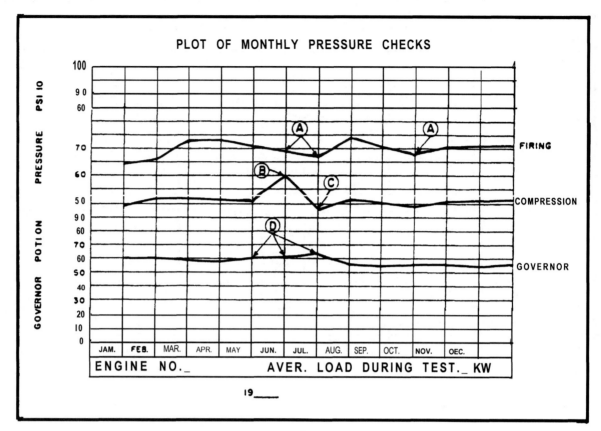

A.

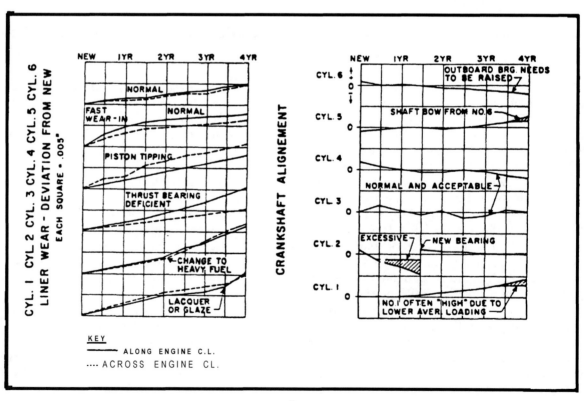

B.

Figure 3-18. Maintenance data plots.
A) 'AS-FOUND" PRESSURES, B) MEASUREMENTS OF MECHANICAL WEAR INDICATORS.

(2) Inspect moving parts as follows:

(a) Crankshaft for out-of-alignment condition; journal surfaces for highly polished condition and absence of scratches, nicks, etc.; and counterweights, gears, and flywheels for proper condition. Verify that crankshaft complies with manufacturer's requirements. An engine crankshaft is a costly and vulnerable component. Special care in handling is required. Accurate alignment is essential to good engine operation. Removal or installation may require hoisting. Refer to the manufacturer's instructions for details and proper procedures.

(b) Main bearings for highly polished condition, cracks, deformation and absence of scratches, nicks, etc.

(c) Thrust bearings for cracks and deformation; surfaces for smoothness and absence of scratches and nicks.

(d) Camshaft cams and cam faces for worn or deformed condition; journal surfaces and bearings for highly polished condition and absence of scratches, nicks, etc; and cam contours and cam followers for good condition.

(e) Connecting rods for cracks or other flaws by magnaflux or dye penetrant method and for bending and for parallelism; bearings for highly polished condition and absence of scratches, nicks, cracks, and deformation.

(f) Pistons for cracks and warped condition; verify pistons, rings, and pins comply with manufacturer's requirements; and rings and pins for general good condition.

(g) Timing gear mechanisms for good condition; backlash for manufacturer's tolerance requirements; and gear teeth for general good condition.

(h) Auxiliary or accessory drives for good operating condition. Consult the specific manufacturer's literature for instructions.

d. Repair parts and supplies. Certain repair parts and supplies must be available for immediate use. Refer to specific manufacturer's literature for recommendations. The following information is a general guide:

(1) The following parts should be renewed at each: gaskets, rubber sleeves, and seals. Adequate quantities should be maintained.

(2) The following parts have a reasonably predictable service life and require replacement at predictable periods: fuel injectors, pumps, governors, and valves. A one-year supply should be maintained.

(3) The following parts have a normally long life and, if failure occurs, could disable the engine for a long period of time: cylinder head, cylinder liner, piston and connecting rod, gear and chain drive parts, and oil pressure pump. One item of each part for an engine should be available.

e. Parts salvage. Certain parts may be replaced prior to their failure due to a preventive maintenance program. It may be possible to restore these parts to specified tolerances. Refer to specific manufacturer's literature for recommendations and instructions. The following information is a general guide:

(1) Worn pump shafts and cylinder liners may be built up and machined to specified dimensions.

(2) Grooves in pistons may be machined and oversize rings specified for use.

(3) Press-fitted bushings and bearings may loosen. The related body part may be machined to a new dimension and oversize bushings and bearings fitted.

(4) Worn journals on crankshafts and camshafts may be built up and machined to specified dimensions.

3-13. Gas turbine engines.

The following provides a general description of gas turbine engines used for power generation. Information is also provided in paragraph 3-1b of this manual. For generating electric power, a turboshaft (shaft turbine) engine is used (see fig 3-19). In a turboshaft engine, the turbine provides power in excess of that required to drive the engine compressor. The excess power is applied as rotary driving torque available at an output shaft. The power to drive the output shaft is extracted from the same turbine that drives the compressor. The turbine is usually connected through a gearbox to the generator. The gearbox is used for speed reduction.

3-14. Gas turbine engine classifications.

a. Pressure and stages. Gas-turbine engines used for auxiliary power generator sets are classified as high-pressure-turbine (HPT) or low-pressure-turbine (LPT) types. Additionally, the engines are classified by the number of stages employed in the turbine design. In general, the more stages used in the design, the greater the engine torque. All of the turbine rotor stages in the multi-stage turbine are connected to a common shaft.

b. Power requirement. For a specified prime mover power requirement, the engine design can be either a single-stage, large diameter turbine or an equivalent small diameter multi-stage turbine.

c. Simple cycle. Most engines are designed to use natural gas and/or liquid fuel similar to kerosene. These are called simple-cycle engines.

d. Compressor and combustor. Most engines have an axial flow compressor and a cannular or annular combustion section (combustor).

3-15. Principles of operation.

a. Components. A typical gas turbine engine consists of a compressor, combustor and turbine (see fig 3-20).

(1) The compressor is driven by the turbine through a common shaft. Air enters the compressor via an inlet duct. The compressor increases the air pressure and reduces the air volume as it pumps air to the combustor and through the engine.

(2) Fuel (liquid and/or natural gas) is delivered to the combustor by a fuel system consisting of a manifold, tubes, and nozzles. Electrical igniters in the combustor provide a spark to ignite the fuel/air mixture for engine start-up. The igniters are deactivated after start-up has been accomplished. Hot combustion gases are expelled through the turbine.

(3) The turbine extracts energy from the hot gases, converting it to rotary power which drives the compressor and any load, such as a generator. Exhaust gases are vented via ductwork to the atmosphere.

(4) The air intake for a gas turbine engine usually consists of a plenum chamber with a screened inlet duct opening. The plenum chamber and duct

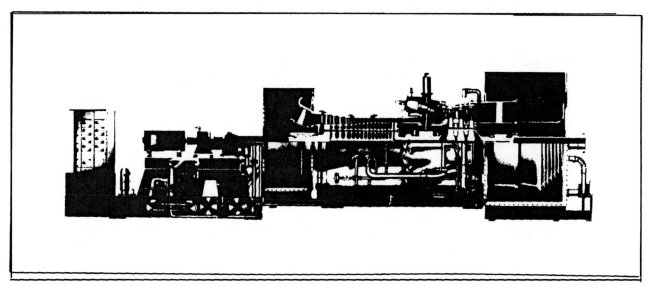

Figure 3-19. Typical gas turbine engine for driving electric power generator.

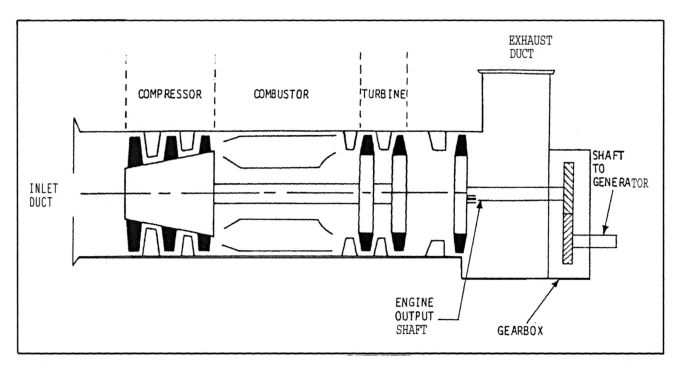

Figure 3-20. Gas turbine engine, turboshaft.

are engine emplacement features that may vary at different installations. Air entering the duct passes through a filter assembly. The filters remove debris and other material that would otherwise be drawn into the engine compressor and other operating areas causing damage. Usually the lowest part of the plenum is equipped with a drain for removal of moisture.

b. *Sequence of euents.* Combustion causes an increase in gas temperature proportionate to the amount of fuel being injected, a moderate increase in velocity, and a negligible decrease in pressure. Approximately 25 percent of the compressor's total air flow is used for combustion at an air/fuel ratio of about 15:1. The remaining 75 percent of compressor air output is fed to the combustor and to cool combustor liners for cooling combustion gases before they enter the turbine.

(1) The sequence of events during turbine engine start-up and operation is as follows:

(a) Air is drawn into the compressor by rotating the engine. Rotation is accomplished by the engine starter. The engine is rotated to the speed at which it becomes self-sustaining.

(b) As the engine shaft is rotated and accelerated by the starter, fuel is fed to the combustor. When the air pressure is high enough, the air/fuel mixture is ignited by an electrical spark.

(c) The electrical spark is deactivated after ignition occurs. Since the air/fuel mixture is continuously fed to the combustor by the turbine and compressor, and since there is a flame in the combustor after ignition, engine operation is self-sustaining.

(d) Rotation of the engine by the starter is necessary after combustion takes place to help accelerate the engine to rated speed. Once the engine speed has increased to approximately 60 percent of rated speed, the starter is deactivated.

(e) Gas turbine engines have dual-fuel capability since they may use either liquid or gaseous fuel. Generating units with these engines are reliable and virtually free of vibration.

(2) Types of combustors. Combustors for gas turbine engines for generators are either cannular or annular-type with newer engines usually having an annular combustor. The annular-type engine is described in this manual. See figure 3-21 for details. The annular combustor consists of a continuous circular inner and outer casing or shell; the space between the casings is open. The cannular combustor consists of inner and outer combustion casings mounted coaxially around the engine compressor/rotor shaft. A cluster of burner cans are located between the two casings. The cans are interconnected by tubes to allow flame propagation during ignition and operation.

3-16. Gas turbine fuel system.

System components. The system provides the engine with the proper amount of fuel to sustain operation. System components include filters, a fuel manifold, fuel tubes, and nozzles. Off-engine components include the fuel control equipment and a supply system.

a. Fuel. Fuel (liquid and/or natural gas) enters the tubular fuel manifold ring via the supply system. The fuel tubes direct the fuel from the manifold to the fuel nozzles which are mounted in the fuel swirlers (see fig 3-22 and 3-23). Compressor discharge air flows radially inward through the primary swirler in the combustion liner, which rotates the air circumferentially and mixes it with the fuel. Air entering radially inward through the secondary swirler is caused to rotate in the opposite direction. As the two counter-rotating mixtures join, the fuel mixes completely with the air. This process promotes complete mixing of the fuel and air and, therefore, more complete burning of the mixture resulting in less smoke emission and more uniform temperature distribution within the combustor.

b. Ignition. Ignition is accomplished by one or two igniter plugs. At ignition, the igniters are activated and fuel is injected into the swirlers. After ignition, the igniters are deactivated (refer to para 3-15b(1)).

3-17. Gas turbine cooling system.

a. Approximately 25 percent of the air entering a combustor is mixed with fuel and burned. The remaining air is mixed with the products of combustion to reduce the temperature of gases entering the turbine to a safe operating level. Cooling is accomplished by engine airflow.

b. Three forms of air cooling of the vanes and blades are used, either separately or in combinations. The types of cooling are convection, impingement, and film (see fig 3-24).

(1) *Convection.* For convection cooling, air flows inside the vanes or blades through serpentine paths and exits through the blade tip or holes in the trailing edge. This form of cooling is used in the area of lower gas temperature (see fig 3-25).

(2) *Impingement.* Impingement cooling is a form of convection cooling, accomplished by directing cooling air against the inside surface of the airfoil through small internal high velocity air jets. Cooling is concentrated at critical sections, such as leading edges of vanes and blades (see fig 3-26).

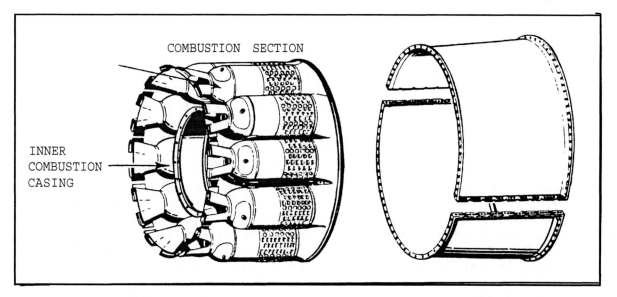

CANNULAR COMBUSTOR   COMBUSTION OUTER CASING

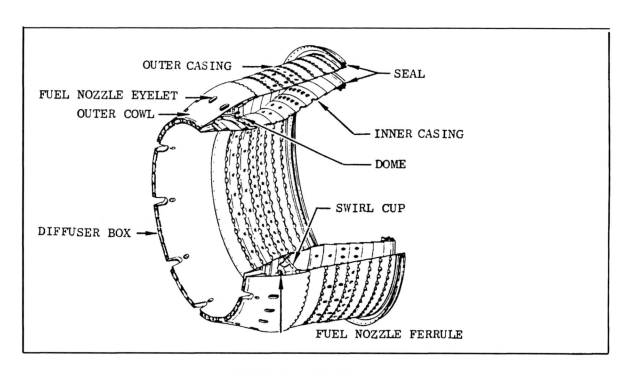

ANNULAR COMBUSTOR

Figure 3-21. Typical types of combustors.
ABOVE: CANNULAR TYPE; BELOW: ANNULAR TYPE

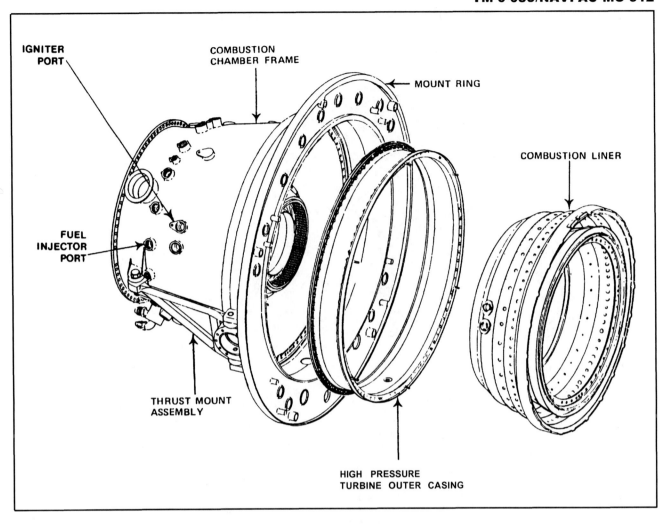

IGNITER PORT

COMBUSTION CHAMBER FRAME

MOUNT RING

COMBUSTION LINER

FUEL INJECTOR PORT

THRUST MOUNT ASSEMBLY

HIGH PRESSURE TURBINE OUTER CASING

Figure 3--22. Engine combustion section.

(3) *Film.* Film cooling is a process whereby a layer of cooling air is maintained between high temperature gases and the external surfaces of the turbine blades and vanes. In general, film cooling is the most effective type.

3-18. Lubrication system.

a. The lubrication system for a gas turbine engine is usually self-contained with the engine and supplies oil for lubrication and cooling during engine operation (see fig 3-27). Engine bearings in the compressor, combustor, and turbine areas (identified as areas A, B, and C, respectively) are supplied by the system. System pressure is approximately 75 psi and is usually maintained by a supply and scavenge pump (refer to scavenging in appendix C). Most systems include a heat exchanger to cool the oil and an oil supply tank.

b. On-engine components usually include lubrication supply and scavenge piping, a supply temperature RTD sensor (resistance temperature detector), and chip detectors at A, B, and/or C oil collection sumps. Nozzles are provided for oil distri-

bution to bearings. Off-engine components include flexible oil lines between on-engine and off-engine components, oil cooler, oil tank, lubrication supply differential pressure sensor, and lubrication pump. Oil is supplied by jet or spray to bearings in other areas via tubes. The engine starter is usually located in an accessory gearbox.

(1) *A-Sump.* Oil for A-sump components is usually piped from a gearbox into the sump. Internal passages and manifolding carry the oil to the A-sump housing. A double-headed nozzle supplies oil to the forward bearing and the undercooled carbon seal runner for the bearing. The second bearing is lubricated through oil nozzles mounted on a power take-off housing. Oil is supplied to the rear bearings through jets on the forward and aft sides of the bearing. The carbon seal runner for the bearing is cooled by oil which has lubricated the power take-off unit and the compressor forward shaft, and is then sprayed outward through holes in the shaft. This oil is then passed through holes at the seal runner where an oil slinger moves it away from the carbon seal.

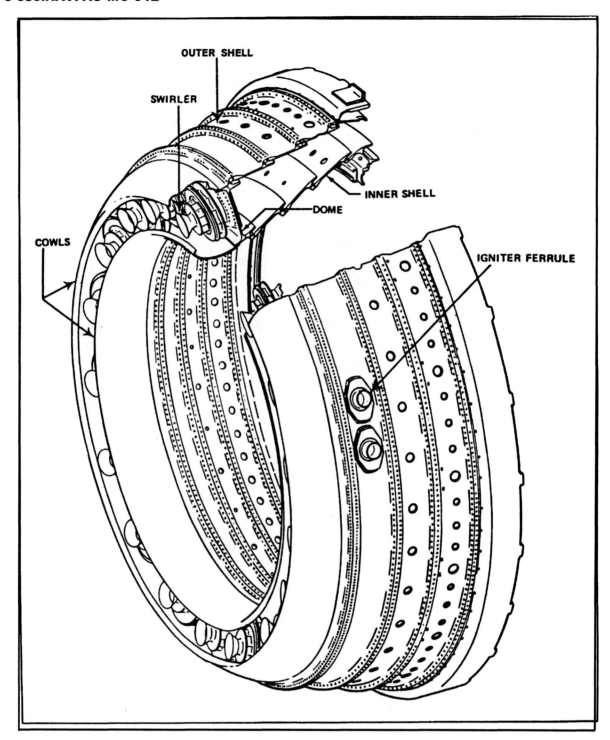

Figure 3-23. Engine combustion liner.

(2) *B-Sump.* Oil enters the B-sump via a frame strut and is directed through tubing in the housing to the mid-engine bearing oil nozzles. Each nozzle has two jets. One jet supplies oil to the bearing and the other jet supplies oil to the carbon seal runner for the bearing.

(3) *C-Sump.* Oil enters the C-sump through a feed tube and is diverted internally through manifolding and tubing to the oil nozzles. In many engines, the rearmost nozzle has two heads with two jets in each head. One set of jets sprays oil on the bearing. The other set sprays oil on the bearing locknut which causes the oil to spray on the rear wall of the C-sump cover and vent collector to cool it and reduce coking. The adjacent bearing oil nozzle also usually has two heads with two jets in each. Two jets direct oil onto the bearing and the others direct oil to the carbon seal runner for the bearing.

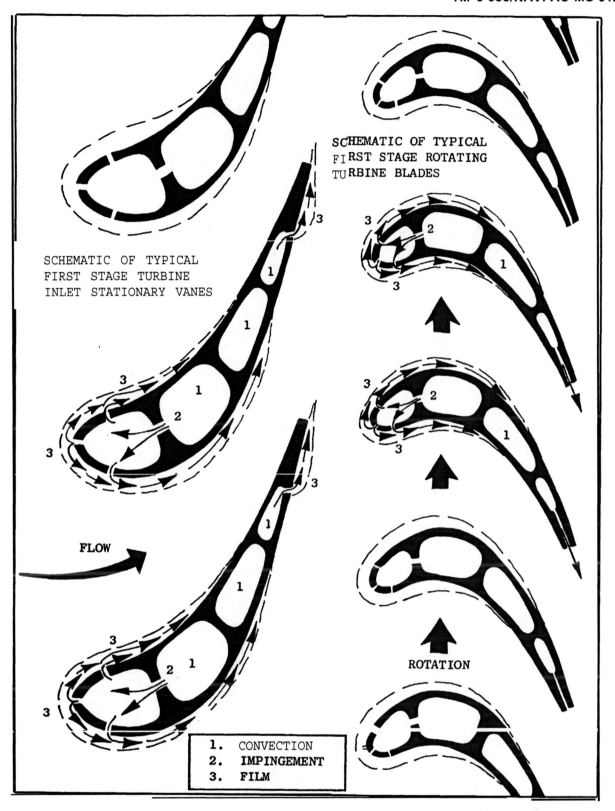

SCHEMATIC OF TYPICAL
FIRST STAGE ROTATING
TURBINE BLADES

SCHEMATIC OF TYPICAL
FIRST STAGE TURBINE
INLET STATIONARY VANES

FLOW

ROTATION

1. CONVECTION
2. IMPINGEMENT
3. FILM

Figure 3-24. Air cooling modes of turbine vanes and blades.

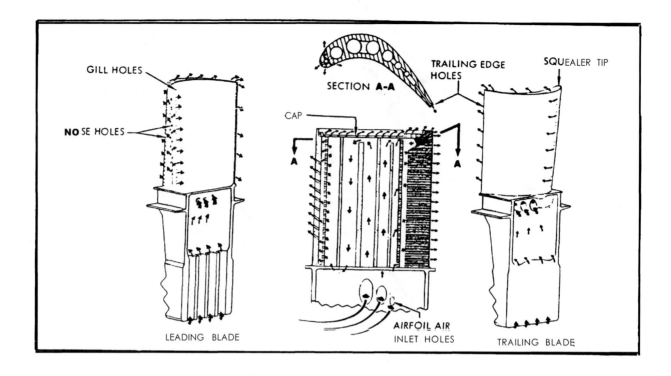

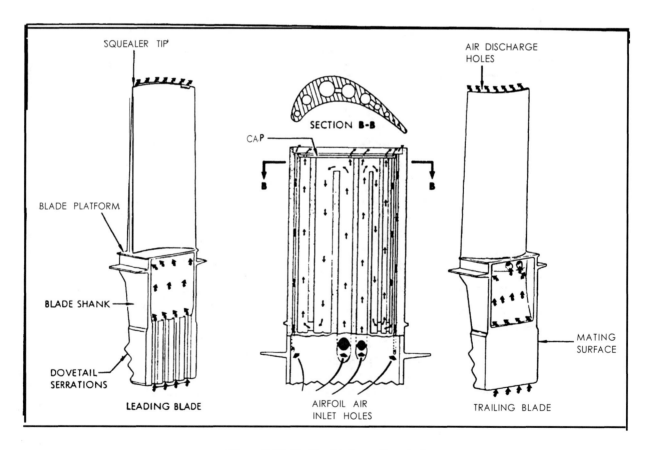

Figure 3-25. Turbine blade cooling air flow.

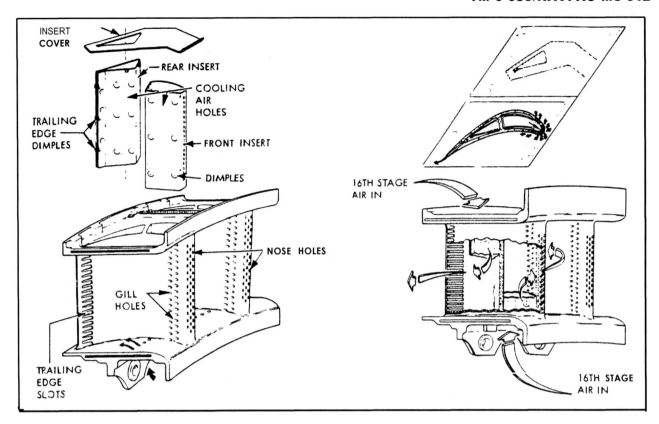

Figure 3-26. Turbine vane cooling air flow.

(4) *Scavenging.* Scavenging is accomplished by a multi-element lubrication and scavenge pump. One element is used for pumping. The other elements are used for forward and aft scavenging of the B-sump and C-sump. Oil in the A-sump drains by gravity into the accessory gearbox.

(5) *Venting.* Some lubrication systems are vented. To maintain high differential pressure across the carbon seals to prevent oil leakage, a high sump vent capacity is required. The A and C sumps vent through the engine output shaft and vent collector to ambient. The B-sump vents to the turbine exhaust gas stream.

3-19. Starting system.

Gas turbine engine starters must be capable of rotating an engine up to a speed-at which it becomes self-sustaining. The starter must provide sufficient torque to accelerate the engine from a standstill to a self-sustaining speed within a specified time. Although it must continue to assist the engine in accelerating up to a predetermined speed.

a. Electric motor. An electric starter motor is usually used for a gas turbine engine in service as an auxiliary generator prime mover. The starter rotates the engine compressor shaft via the gear train in the accessory gearbox. In most installations the starter can be energized either automatically or manually.

b. Fuel. As the engine is accelerated by the starter, fuel is supplied when a specified rotational speed is attained. When this speed is attained, the compressor and engine-driven fuel pump will deliver sufficient air and fuel, respectively to the combustion chamber to sustain satisfactory combustion.

c. Ignition system. An ignition system, consisting of an ignition exciter, igniter plug lead assemblies, and igniter plugs, is required. Fuel ignition is ensured by one or two igniter plugs connected to the exciter by the separate igniter leads. The plugs are located in the combustion chamber. Each plug consists of center and outer electrodes with a semiconductor surface coating at the tip between the two electrodes. The semiconductor ma.terial is used as a shunt to aid in ionizing the air gap between the two electrodes so that the plugs will fire. An air shroud covers the end of the plug immersed in the air stream for cooling.

d. Specialized system. Starting systems are highly specialized and are usually applicable to a given installation or site. Refer to supplier's on-site technical literature for details.

3-20. Governor/speed control.

a. Engine operation. The engine is started by an external power source. Once the engine reaches idle speed, it is self-sustaining. All it needs is adequate supplies of air and fuel. Combustion gas drives the

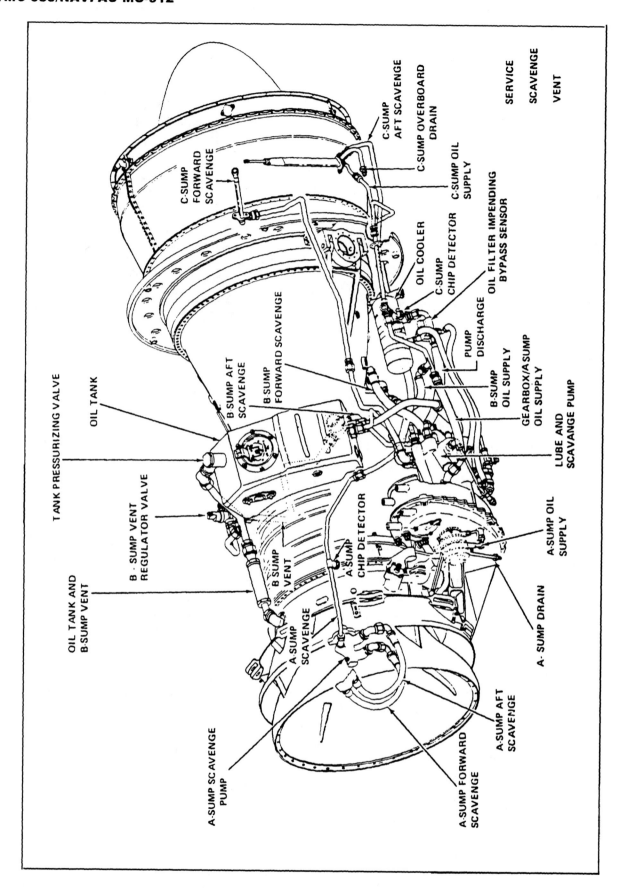

Figure 3-27. Lubrication system for gas turbine.

turbine which is mounted on a common shaft with the compressor. The compressor draws in the air for combustion and also drives the gearbox gear train. About two-thirds of the power derived from combustion is required to sustain combustion. The remaining power is available for work purposes and drives the output shaft.

b. Speed signal. An engine speed signal, generated by magnetic pickups (speed transducers) in the gearbox, provides electrical signals that are proportional to engine speed. The signal causes a dc voltage to be generated.

c. Thermocouples. Thermocouples sense the turbine discharge/inlet total temperature. The electrical temperature sensing signal is an average of the operating temperature profile.

d. Pressure sensing. Sensing of compressor discharge static pressure and turbine discharge pressure is also required for engine speed control. These pressures are combined to produce an electrical signal equal to pressure ratio.

e. Computer. The three signals (speed, temperature, and pressure ratio) are summed in an acceleration/deceleration computer. Computer output functions with a governor to meter fuel required for engine operation. If required, a signal derived from a tachometer can be used to determine a rate-of-change feedback signal.

3-21. Compressor.

The function of the compressor is to raise the pressure and reduce the volume of the air as it pumps it through the engine. An axial flow or centrifugal flow compressor is used. Most engines use a multistage, axial flow compressor such as described herein. The axial flow consists of two major subassemblies: the rotor assembly and the stator assembly. Axial flow compressor efficiency is better than centrifugal flow compressor efficiency. Centrifugal flow compressors were first used in early design gas turbine engines. The main component is an impeller which is mounted on a common shaft with the turbine. These compressors are generally used with smaller engines and have a fairly low pressure ratio. The design has lower efficiency than the axial-flow design but is less expensive to manufacture.

3-22. Gas turbine service practices.

a. Maintenance program. Service practices for gas turbine engines consist of a complete mainte-nance program that is built around records and observation. The program is described in the manufacturer's literature furnished with each engine. It includes appropriate analysis of these records.

b. Record keeping. Engine log sheets are an important part of record keeping. The sheets must be developed to suit individual applications (i.e., auxiliary use) and related instrumentation.

c. Log sheet data. Log sheets should include engine starts and stops, fuel and lubrication oil consumption, and a record of the following:

(1) Hours since last oil change.

(2) Hours since first put in service or last overhaul.

(3) Total hours on engine.

d. Oil analysis program. Use of a Spectrometric Oil Analysis Program is recommended to determine the internal condition of the engine's oil-wetted (wear metal) components, such as bearings, gears, and lubrication pump.

(1) The program should be used as a supplement to the regular maintenance procedure of chip detection and filter inspection. Normal wear causes microscopic metal particles (smaller than one micron) to mix with the lubricating oil and remain in suspension. Samples of oil taken from the engine after a shutdown will contain varying amounts of wear-metal particles.

(2) Oil samples should be removed from the engine at the time intervals specified by the engine manufacturer. A sample should always be taken from the same location on the engine (this may vary from each engine). Refer to manufacturer's literature. See appendix C paragraph C-le(2).

(a) Metal content. Evaluation of the oil's wear-metal content is very important. The quantity of wear-metal in the sample as well as type (iron or steel, silver, chromium, nickel, etc.) must be evaluated and recorded.

(b) failure forecast. Evaluation records are intended as an aid in forecasting what components are in danger of failing. Contamination of the oil sample must be prevented to avoid false indication of engine internal conditions.

e. Industrial practices. Use recognized industrial practices as the general guide for engine servicing. Service information is provided in manufacturer's literature and appendixes B through G.

f. Reference Literature. The engine user should refer to manufacturer's literature for specific information on individual units.

CHAPTER 4

GENERATORS AND EXCITERS

4-1. Electrical energy.

Mechanical energy provided by a prime mover is converted into electrical energy by the generator (see fig 4-l). The prime mover rotates the generator rotor causing magnetic lines of force to be cut by electrical conductors. Electrical energy is thereby produced by electromagnetic induction. The ratio of output energy generated by input energy is expressed as a percentage and always shows a loss in efficiency.

4-2. Generator operation.

a. A generator consists of a number of conducting coils and a magnetic field. The coils are called the armature. Relative motion between the coils and magnetic field induces voltage in the coils. This action is called electromotive force (emf). A schematic for a typical generator system is shown in figure 4-2.

b. An alternating current (AC) generator needs a separate direct current (DC) source to feed the magnetic field. The required DC is provided by an external source called an exciter. Usually, the exciter is a small DC generator that is driven by the generator rotor. The exciter may be mounted on the rotor shaft or rotated by belt-drive. Some generating systems use a static, solid-state exciter to provide DC.

c. A voltage regulator controls the induced voltage by regulating the strength of the electromagnetic field established by the exciter. Frequency is controlled by the speed at which the prime mover rotates the rotor.

4-3. Types of generators.

Depending on the type of generating equipment employed, the electrical energy produced is either direct current (DC) or alternating current (AC).

a. AC generators. AC generators are classified as single-phase or polyphase. A single-phase generator is usually limited to 25 kW or less and generates AC power at a specific utilization voltage. Polyphase generators produce two or more alternating voltages (usually two, three, or six phases).

b. DC generators. DC generators are classified as either shunt, series, or compound-wound. Most DC generators are the compound-wound type. Shunt generators are usually used as battery chargers and as exciters for AC generators. Series generators are sometimes used for street lights. The emf induced in a DC generator coil is alternating. Rectification is

needed to direct the flow of current in one direction. The generator rotating commutator provides the rectifying action.

4-4. AC generators.

a. AC generators are considered either brush or brushless, based on the method used to transfer DC exciting current to the generator field. In addition, AC generators are classified as salient-pole or nonsalient-pole depending on the configuration of the field poles. Projecting field poles are salient-pole units and turbo-type (slotted) field poles are nonsalient-pole units. Typical AC generator armatures are shown in figures 4-3 and 4-4.

b. Damper windings on the rotor stabilize the speed of the AC generator to reduce hinting under changing loads. If the speed tends to increase, induction-generator action occurs in the damper windings. This action places a load on the rotor, tending to slow the machine down. If the speed tends to decrease, induction-motor action occurs in the damper winding, tending to speed the machine up. The windings are copper bars located in the faces of the rotor pole pieces. Mounted parallel to the rotor axis, the bars are connected at each end by a copper ring.

c. AC generators that operate at a speed that is exactly proportional to the frequency of the output voltage are synchronous generators. Synchronous generators are usually called alternators.

4-5. Alternator types.

Alternators are single-phase or polyphase. Variations include three-phase alternators used as single-phase units by insulating and not using one phase lead. Since the lead is unused, it is not brought out to a terminal. The kilowatt rating is reduced from that of the three-phase unit as limited by the amount of current carried by a coil. An alternator designed only for single-phase operation usually does not have coils in all of the armature slots because end coils contribute little to the output voltage and increase the coil impedance in the same proportion as any other coil.

(a) Single-phase alternators are usually used in smaller systems (limited to 25kW or less) and produce AC power at utilization voltages.

(1) Terminal voltage is usually 120 volts. The electric load is connected across the terminals with protective fuses. One voltmeter and one ammeter measure the output in volts and amperes, respec-

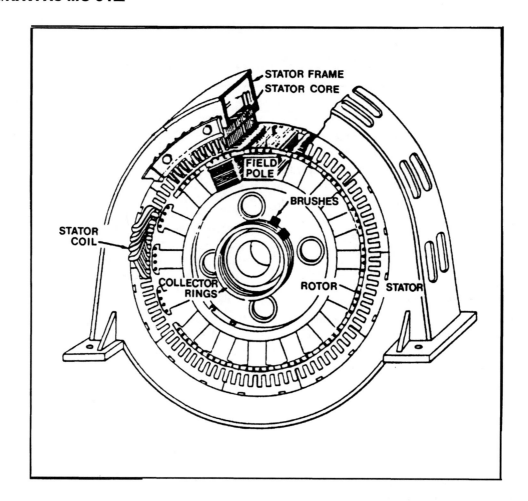

Figure 4-l. Typical alternating current generator.

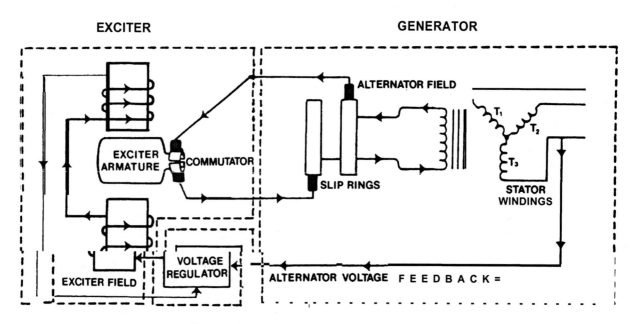

Figure 4-2. Brush-type excitation system, schematic.

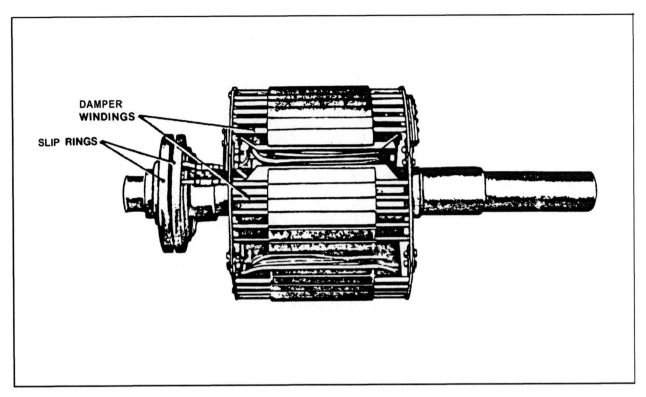

Figure 4-3. Brush-type AC generator field and rotor:

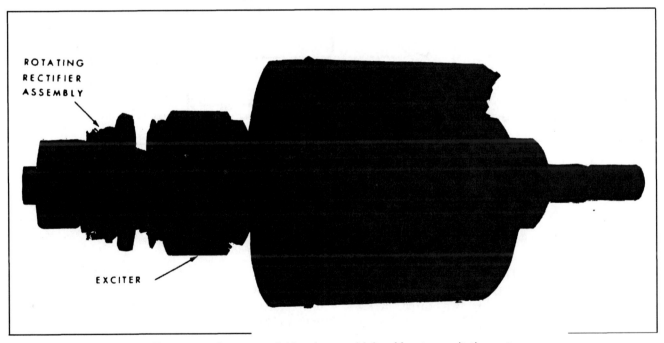

Figure 4-4. AC generator field and rotor with brushless-type excitation system.

tively The two-wire alternator has two power terminals, one for each end of the armature coil (see fig 4-5).

(2) The three-wire, single-phase alternator has three power terminals; one from each end of the armature coil and one from the midpoint (neutral, see fig 4-6). Terminal voltage is usually 120 volts from the midpoint to either end of the armature coil

and 240 volts between the two ends. The load is connected between the two outside wires or between either outside wire and neutral, depending upon the voltage required by the load. Assuming alternator voltage to be 120/240 volts, load 1,0 and load 2,0 would consist of 120-volt lamps and 120-volt single-phase power equipment. Load 1,2 would consist of 240-volt power equipment. Two voltmeters and two

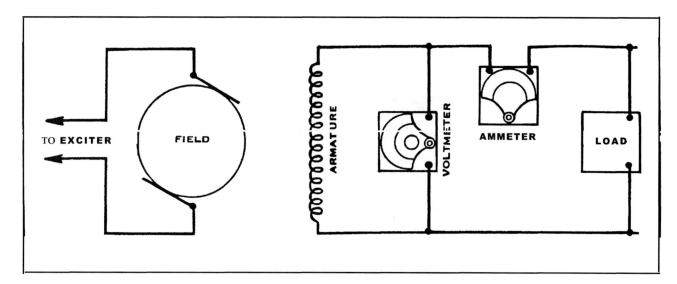

Figure 4-5. Two-wire, single-phase alternator.

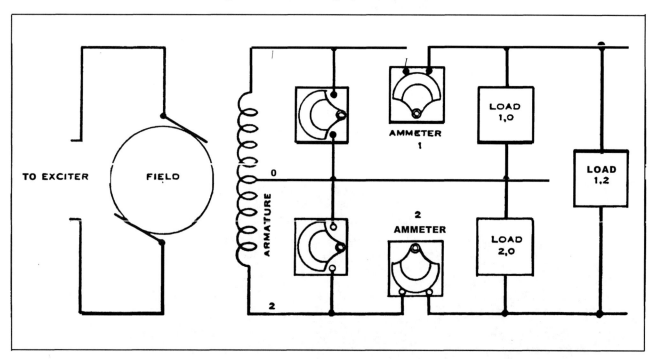

Figure 4-6. Three-wire, single-phase alternator.

ammeters (or equivalent) are required to determine the load in kilovoltamperes (kVA).

(b) Polyphase alternators are two, three, or six phases. Two-phase power is used in only a few localities. Six-phase is primarily used for operation of rotary converters or large rectifiers. Three-phase alternators are the most widely used for power production. Polyphase alternators have capacities from 3 kW to 250,000 kW and voltage from 110 V to 13,800 V. Two general types of three-phases alternator windings are the delta winding used in three-wire, three-phase alternators, and the star or wye winding used in four-wire, three-phase types. Three-wire, three-phase alternators have three sets

of single-phase windings spaced 120 electrical degrees apart around the armature. One electrical degree is equivalent to one degree of arc in a two-pole machine, 0.50 degree of arc in a four-pole machine, 0.33 degree of arc in a six-pole machine, and so on. The three single-phase windings are connected in series to form the delta connection, and the terminals are connected to the junction point of each pair of armature coils (see fig 4-7). The total current in a delta-connected circuit is always equal to the vector sum of currents in two-phase windings. The instantaneous current flows out to the load through two windings and returns from the load through the third winding. Since the coils are

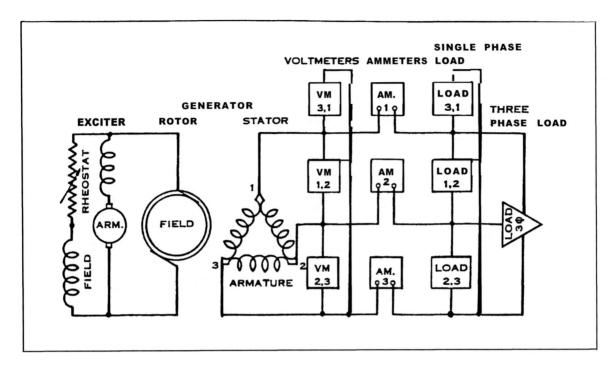

Figure 7.92 Three-wire, three-phase alternator.

similar physically and electrically, equal voltages are generated and applied to the terminals. Due to spacing of the coils about the armature, the maximum voltage between the pairs of terminals does not occur simultaneously. The characteristics of three- wire, three-phase (or delta) alternators are:

(1) The amount of current through the alternator terminals is the algebraic sum of current through the alternator coils.

(2) The currents are not equal in magnitude or time.

(3) Connection between coils can be made either inside or outside the generator.

(c) In a 60-Hertz machine, each coil experiences maximum instantaneous voltage, first positive and then negative, 120 times each second. Disregarding voltage direction, the maximum instantaneous voltages occur on successive coils 0.003 seconds apart. Due to time differences between the voltages and resulting currents, the amount of current through the alternator terminals and the amount through the alternator coils are not equal in magnitude or time. The current through the alternator is 73 percent greater than through the coils. Coil and terminal voltages are the same magnitude. Three voltmeters and three ammeters (or equivalent) are required to measure the load on the alternator. The average value of the three currents times the average value of the three voltages plus 73 percent gives a close approximation of the alternator load in kilovolt-amperes. Two single-phase or one two-element polyphase kilowatt-hour meter is required to measure the alternator output in kilowatt-hours.

(d) The four-wire, three-phase alternator (see fig 4-8) has three sets of armature coils spaced 120 electrical degrees apart about the armature, the same as the three-wire, three-phase alternator. One end of each of the three coils is connected to a common terminal (neutral). The other end of each coil is connected to separate terminals (phase terminals). Thus, the four-wire alternator has four terminals which connect to the three-phase conductors and the neutral of the power-plant bus. When each end of each coil is brought out to separate terminals, the connections between coils are made outside of the alternator, enabling installation of a more comprehensive protective relaying system.

(e) The four-wire, three-phase alternator can be connected to a transformer instead of the power-plant bus by using a wye-wye transformation. Irregular (double or triple) harmonics, which may be produced, can be suppressed by using a core-type transformer. A third or tertiary winding with a delta connection may also be used as a suppressor. A wye-delta transformer may be used if the power plant bus is three wire and the alternator is four wire wye connected.

(f) Four-wire three-phase, dual voltage and frequency alternators are also used. These are supplied in sizes from 15 to 1500 kW, 127-220 volts, three-phase, 60 Hertz, or 230-400 volts, three-phase, 50 Hertz. Dual stator coils are used on each phase. Coil ends are brought out to a terminal board for making connections. Voltage and frequency combinations are shown in figure 4-9.

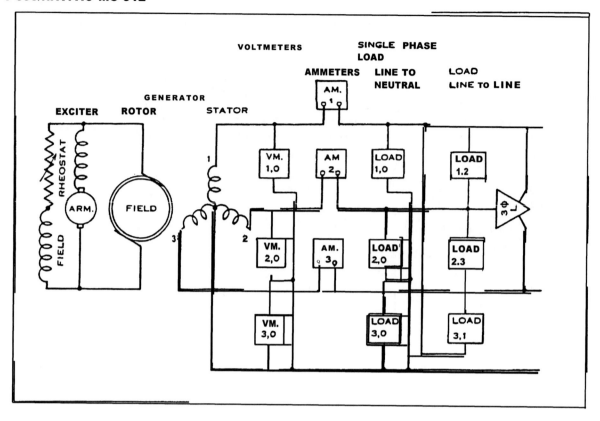

Figure 4-8. Four-wire, three-phase alternator.

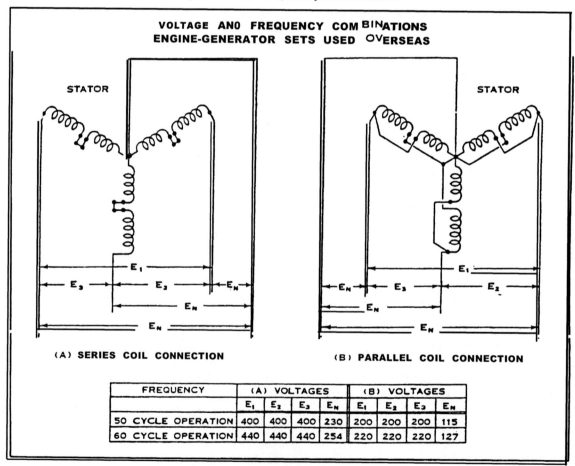

VOLTAGE AND FREQUENCY COMBINATIONS
ENGINE-GENERATOR SETS USED OVERSEAS

FREQUENCY	(A) VOLTAGES				(B) VOLTAGES			
	E_1	E_2	E_3	E_N	E_1	E_2	E_3	E_N
50 CYCLE OPERATION	400	400	400	230	200	200	200	115
60 CYCLE OPERATION	440	440	440	254	220	220	220	127

Figure 4-9. Dual voltage and frequency.

(g) Most parts of the world have standardized on either 50 or 60 Hertz alternating current power. Sixty Hertz power is commonly used in the United States. Fifty Hertz power is used in many countries outside the United States. The ratio between the 60-50 Hertz frequencies is 6:5. Electrical energy received at one frequency can be converted to a different frequency by using a frequency changer. If a large power requirement exists, it may be more economical to use a special alternator to produce power at the desired frequency The applicable equation is:

$$V = K \times \emptyset \times N \times f$$

where V = generated voltage
K = constant value number (speed)
∅ = phase/phase angle
N = number of turns
f = line frequency

(h) The generated voltage is proportional to the strength of the magnetic field, phase, and number of turns in series between terminals and the speed.

4-6. Design.

a. Components. A typical AC generator consists of a stationary stator and a rotor mounted within the stator (see fig 4-1). The stator contains a specific number of coils, each with a specific number of windings. Similarly, the rotor consists of a specific number of field poles, each with a specific number of windings. In addition to the rotor and stator (refer to paragraphs 4-6b and 4-6c, respectively), a generator has a collector assembly (usually consisting of collector slip rings, brushes, and brush holders). The slip rings are covered in paragraph 4-6d. DC flows from the exciter, through the negative brush and slip ring, to the rotor field poles. The return path to the exciter is through the positive brush and slip ring.

b. Rotor. The rotor contains magnetic fields which are established and fed by the exciter. When the rotor is rotated, AC is induced in the stator. The changing polarity of the rotor produces the alternating characteristics of the current. The generated voltage is proportional to the strength of the magnetic field, the number of coils (and number of windings of each coil), and the speed at which the rotor turns.

c. Stator. The frame assembly is the main component of the stator. Insulated windings (or coils) are placed in slots near an air gap in the stator core. There is a fixed relationship between the unit's number of phases and the way the coils are connected. The stator in a four-wire, three-phase unit has three sets of armature coils which are spaced 120 electrical degrees apart. One end of each coil is connected to a common neutral terminal. The other

end of each coil is connected to separate terminals. Conductors attached to the four terminals carry the current to the system's switchgear and on to the load.

d. Collector slip rings. Slip rings are usually made of nonferrous metal (brass, bronze or copper); iron or steel is sometimes used. Slip rings usually do not require much servicing. The wearing of grooves or ridges in the slip rings is retarded by designing the machine with limited endplay and by staggering the brushes. Surfaces of the slip rings should be bright and smooth, polishing can be performed with fine sandpaper and honing stone. Electrolytic action can occur at slip ring surfaces producing formation of verdigris. Verdigris is a greenish coating that forms on nonferrous metals. Electrolytic deterioration can be prevented by reversing the polarity of the slip rings once or twice a year. The stator of the three-wire, three-phase unit also has three sets of armature coils spaced 120 electrical degrees apart. The ends of the coils are connected together in a delta configuration. Conductors are attached to the three connecting points.

4-7. Characteristics of generators.

a. Voltage. Generated voltage is the emf denoting the electric pressure between phases in the armature. The magnetic flux linking each armature coil changes as the machine rotates. The change in flux per turn occurs at the conductors in the armature slots. Each conductor is regarded separately as it cuts the flux. At a specific rotating speed, instantaneous volts per conductor are proportional to air gap flux density at the conductor.

b. Current. Current is the rate of transfer (flow) of electricity, expressed in amperes. Field current required for a particular load condition, is determined by the magnetic circuit, in conjunction with armature and field windings. Load current is equal to the generated voltage divided by the impedance of the load.

c. Speed. Normally, a generator operates at a constant speed corresponding to the frequency and number of poles. Variations may occur due to changes in driving torque, load, field excitation, or terminal voltage.

d. Frequency. AC frequency is determined by the rotating speed and number of poles of the generator. Frequency is usually expressed in Hertz, the frequency used most is 60 Hertz. A two-pole generator must operate at 3600 rpm to maintain 60 Hertz. Four-pole and six-pole units must operate at 1800 rpm and 1200 rpm, respectively, to maintain 60 Hertz. Frequency at 60 Hertz is expressed in the following equation:

$$\text{Frequency} = \frac{\text{(Speed in rpm) (Pairs of poles)}}{60}$$
(60 Hertz)

e. Power. Power is the term used to describe the rate at which electric energy is delivered by a generator and it is usually expressed in watts or kilo-watts (10^3 watts).

(1) *Watts.* Watts are units of active or working power, computed as follows: volts x measured or apparent amperes x power factor.

(2) *Volt amperes reactance (Mars).* Vars are units of reactive or nonworking power (1 var = 1 reactive volt-ampere).

(3) *Power factor.* Power factor is the ratio of active or working power divided by apparent power. The relationship of apparent power, active power, and reactive power is shown in figure 4-10. The hypotenuse represents apparent power, the base represents active power, and the altitude of the power triangle represents reactive power. Power factor (the cosine of angle $\emptyset$) is a unitless number which can be expressed in per unit or in percentage. For convenience, kilo (10^3) is often used with the terms volt- amperes, watts and vars in order to reduce the number of significant digits.

$$\% \text{ Power Factor} = \frac{kW}{kVA} \text{ x } 100$$

4-8. Exciters.

a. An AC or DC generator requires direct current to energize its magnetic field. The DC field current is obtained from a separate source called an exciter. Either rotating or static-type exciters are used for AC power generation systems. There are two types of rotating exciters: brush and brushless. The primary difference between brush and brushless exciters is the method used to transfer DC exciting current to the generator fields. Static excitation for the generator fields is provided in several forms including field-flash voltage from storage batteries and voltage from a system of solid-state components. DC generators are either separately excited or self-excited.

b. Excitation systems in current use include direct-connected or gear-connected shaft-driven DC generators, belt-driven or separate prime mover or motor-driven DC generators, and DC supplied through static rectifiers.

c. The brush-type exciter can be mounted on the same shaft as the AC generator armature or can be housed separately from, but adjacent to, the generator (see fig 4-2). When it is housed separately, the exciter is rotated by the AC generator through a drive belt.

d. The distinguishing feature of the brush-type generator is that stationary brushes are used to transfer the DC exciting current to the rotating generator field. Current transfer is made via rotating slip rings (collector rings) that are in contact with the brushes.

e. Each collector ring is a hardened-steel forging that is mounted on the exciter shaft. Two collector rings are used on each exciter, each ring is fully insulated from the shaft and each other. The inner ring is usually wired for negative polarity, the outer ring for positive polarity.

f. A rotating-rectifier exciter is one example of brushless field excitation. In rotating-rectifier exciters, the brushes and slip rings are replaced by a rotating, solid-state rectifier assembly (see fig 4-4). The exciter armature, generator rotating assembly, and rectifier assembly are mounted on a common shaft. The rectifier assembly rotates with, but is

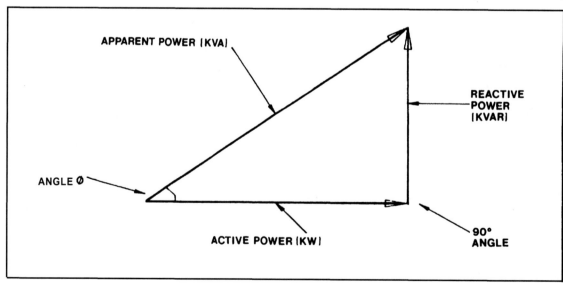

Figure 4-10. Power triangle.

insulated from, the generator shaft as well as from each winding.

g. Static exciters contain no moving parts. A portion of the AC from each phase of generator output is fed back to the field windings, as DC excitations, through a system of transformers, rectifiers, and reactors. An external source of DC is necessary for initial excitation of the field windings. On engine-driven generators, the initial excitation may be obtained from the storage batteries used to start the engine or from control voltage at the switchgear.

4-9. Characteristics of exciters.

a. Voltage. Exciter voltages in common use include 63 and 125 volts for small units and 250, 375, or 500 volts for large units. Exciters with normal self-excitation are usually rated at about 135 percent of rated voltage and a rate buildup of about 125 volts per second. Working range is between 75 and 125 percent of rated exciter voltage.

b. Current. An exciter provides direct current to energize the magnetic field of an AC generator. Any DC generator or storage battery may be used as a field current source.

c. Speed. Speed, in rotating exciters, is related to generator output voltage. Usually, if magnetic field intensity is increased (by higher rotating speed), output voltage of the generator is also increased.

d. Power. Exciter voltage to the magnetic field of an AC generator is usually set at a predetermined value. A voltage regulator controls the generator voltage by regulating the strength of the magnetic field produced in the exciter.

4-10. Field flashing.

a. Field flashing is required when generator voltage does not build up and the generating system (including the voltage regulator) does not have field-flash capability. This condition is usually caused by insufficient residual magnetism in the exciter and generator fields. In some cases, a generator that has been out-of-service for an extended period may lose its residual magnetism and require flashing. Residual magnetism can be restored by flashing the field thereby causing a current surge in the generator. Refer to the voltage regulator manufacturer's literature for procedural instructions.

b. Solid-state components may be included in the voltage regulator. Perform field flashing according to the manufacturer's instructions to avoid equipment damage.

4-11. Bearings and lubrication.

a. Location. Several types of bearings, each with specific lubrication requirements, are used on the generators. Usually, a generator has two bearings, one to support each end of the armature shaft. On some generators, one end of the shaft is supported by the coupling to the prime mover and one bearing is used at the other end. The selections of bearing type and lubrication are based on generator size, type of coupling to prime mover, and expected usage. A generator is usually equipped with either sleeve or ball bearings which are mounted in end shields attached to the generator frame.

b. Sleeve bearings. Sleeve bearings are usually bronze and are lubricated with oil.

(1) Most units with sleeve-type bearings have a reservoir for the oil and a sight gauge to verify oil level. Bearings and the reservoir are fully enclosed.

(2) Distribution of oil to shaft and bearings from the reservoir is by an oil-slinger ring mounted on the generator shaft. Rotation of the slinger ring throws the oil to the top of the bearing. Holes in the bearing admit oil for lubrication.

(3) Some units with sleeve-type bearings have an absorbent fiber packing, saturated with oil, which surrounds the bearing. Holes in the bearing admit oil for lubrication.

c. Ball bearings. Ball bearings (or roller-type bearings) are fully enclosed and lubricated with grease.

(1) Most units with ball or roller-type bearings are equipped with a fitting at each bearing to apply fresh grease. Old grease is emitted from a hoie (normally closed by a plug or screw) in the bearing enclosure.

(2) Some units are equipped with prepacked, lifetime lubricated bearings.

d. Bearing wear. Noise during generator operation may indicate worn bearings. If source of noise is the generator bearing, replacement of the worn bearing is recommended.

e. Service practices. Service practices for generators and exciters consist of a complete maintenance program that is built around records and observations. The program is described in the manufacturer's literature furnished with the component. It includes appropriate analysis of these records.

f. Record keeping. Generator system log sheets are an important part of record keeping. The sheets must be developed to suit individual applications (i.e., auxiliary use).

g. Log sheet data. Log sheets should include system starts and stops and a cumulative record of typical equipment operational items as follows:

(1) Hours of operation since last bearing lubrication.

(2) Hours of operation since last brush and spring inspection or servicing.

(3) Days since last ventilating and cooling screen and duct cleaning.

h. Industrial practices. Use recognized industrial practices as the general guide for generator system servicing.

i. Reference Literature. The generator system user should refer to manufacturer's literature for specific information on individual units.

4-12. Generator maintenance.

a. Service and troubleshooting. Service consists of performing basic and preventive maintenance checks that are outlined below. If troubles develop or if these actions do not correct a problem, refer to the troubleshooting table 4-1. Maintenance personnel must remember that the manufacturer's literature supersedes the information provided herein.

b. Operational check. Check the equipment during operation and observe the following indications.

(1) Unusual noises or noisy operation may indicate excessive bearing wear or faulty bearing alignment. Shut down and investigate.

(2) Equipment overheats or smokes. Shut down and investigate.

(3) Equipment brushes spark frequently. Occasional sparking is normal, but frequent sparking indicates dirty commutator and/or brush or brush spring defects. Shut down and investigate.

c. Preventive maintenance. Inspect the equipment as described once a month. Maintenance personnel should make a check list suited to their particular needs. The actions listed in table 4-l are provided as a guide and may be modified. Refer to manufacturer's instructions.

Table 4-l. Generator inspection list.

Inspect	Check For
Brushes	Amount of wear, Improper wear, Spring Tension
Commutator	Dirt, Amount of wear, Loose leads, Loose bars
Collector Rings	Grooves or wear. Dirt, carbon, and/or copper accumulation. Greenish coating (verdigris)
Insulation	Damaged insulation. Measure and record insulation resistance.
Windings	Dust and dirt, Loose windings or connections
Bearings	Loose shaft or excessive endplay. Vibration (defective bearing)
Bearing Housing	Lubricant leakage, Dirt or sludge in oil (sleeve bearings)
Ventilation and cooling system	Obstruction of air ducts or screens. Loose or bent fan blades

d. Troubleshooting. Perform general troubleshooting of the equipment (as outlined in the following table) if a problem develops. Refer to the manufacturer's literature for repair information after diagnosis.

Table 4-2. Generator trouble shooting.

NOISY OPERATION	
Cause	Remedy
Unbalanced load or coupling misalignment	Balance load and check alignment
Air gap not uniform	Center rotor by replacing or shimming bearings
Coupling loose	Tighten coupling
OVERHEATING	
Electrical load unbalanced	Balance load
Open line fuse	Replace line fuse
Restricted ventilation	Clean, remove obstructions
Rotor winding shorted. opened or grounded	Repair or replace defective coil
Stator winding shorted, opened or grounded	Repair or replace defective coil
Dry bearings	Lubricate
Insufficient heat transfer of cooler unit	Verify design flow rate: repair or replace
NO OUTPUT VOLTAGE	
Stator coil open or shorted	Repair or replace coil
Rotor coils open or shorted	Repair or replace coils
Shorted sliprings	Repair as directed by manufacturer
Internal moisture (indicated by low-resistance reading on megger)	Dry winding
Voltmeter defective	Replace
Ammeter shunt open	Replace ammeter and shunt
OUTPUT VOLTAGE UNSTEADY	
Poor commutation	Clean slip rings and reseat brushes
Loose terminal connections	Clean and tighten all contacts
Fluctuating load	Adjust voltage regulator and governor speed
OUTPUT VOLTAGE TOO HIGH	
Over-excited	Adjust voltage regulator
One leg of delta-connected stator open	Replace or repair defective coils
FREQUENCY INCORRECT OF FLUCTUATING	
Speed incorrect or fluctuating	Adjust speed-governing device

Table 4-2. Generator trouble shooting-Continued

VOLTAGE HUNTING

Cause	Remedy
External field resistance in out position	Adjust resistance
Voltage regulator contacts dirty	Clean and reseat contacts

STATOR OVERHEATS IN SPOTS

Cause	Remedy
Open phase winding	Cut open coil out of circuit and replace at first opportunity. Cut and replace the same coil from other phases
Rotor not centered	Realign and replace bearings, if necessary
Unbalanced circuits	Balance circuits
Loose connections or wrong polarity coil connections	Tighten connections or correct wrong connections
Shorted coil	Cut coil out of circuit and replace at first opportunity

FIELD OVERHEATING

Cause	Remedy
Shorted field coil	Replace or repair
Improper ventilation	Remove obstruction, clean air ducts

ALTERNATOR PRODUCES SHOCK WHEN TOUCHED

Cause	Remedy
Reversed field coil	Check polarity. Change coil leads
Static charge	High-speed belts build up a static charge Connect alternator frame to a ground strip

4-13. Insulation testing.

a. The failure of an insulation system is the most common cause of problems in electrical equipment. Insulation is subject to many effects which can cause it to fail; such as mechanical damage, vibration, excessive heat or cold, dirt, oil, corrosive vapors, moisture from processes, or just the humidity on a muggy day. As pin holes or cracks develop, moisture and foreign matter penetrate the surfaces of the insulation, providing a low resistance path for leakage current. Sometimes the drop in insulation resistance is sudden, as when equipment is flooded. Usually, however, it drops gradually, giving plenty of warning, if checked periodically. Such checks permit planned reconditioning before service failure. If there are no checks, a motor with poor insulation, for example, may not only be dangerous to touch when voltage is applied, but also be subject to burn-out.

b. The electrical test most often conducted to determine the quality of armature and alternator field winding insulation is the insulation resistance test. It is a simple, quick, convenient and nondestructive test that can indicate the contamination of insulation by moisture, dirt or carbonization. There are other tests available to determine the quality of insulation, but they are not recommended because they are generally too complex or destructive. An insulation resistance test should be conducted immediately following generator shutdown when the windings are still hot and dry. A megohmmeter is the recommended test equipment.

c. Before testing the insulation, adhere to the following:

(1) Take the equipment to be tested out of service. This involves deenergizing the equipment and disconnecting it from other equipment and circuits.

(2) If disconnecting the equipment from the circuit cannot be accomplished, then inspect the installation to determine what equipment is connected and will be included in the test. Pay particular attention to conductors that lead away from the installation. This is very important because the more equipment that is included in a test, the lower the reading will be, and the true insulation resistance of the apparatus in question may be masked by that of the associated equipment. It is always possible, of course, that the insulation resistance of the complete installation will be satisfactory, especially for a spot check. Or, it may be higher than the range of the megohmmeter, in which case nothing would be gained by separating the components because the insulation resistance of each part would be still higher.

(3) Test for foreign or induced voltages with a volt-ohm-milliammeter. Pay particular attention once again to conductors that lead away from the circuit being tested and make sure they have been properly disconnected from any source of voltage.

(4) Large electrical equipment and cables usually have sufficient capacitance to store a dangerous amount of energy from the test current. Therefore, discharge capacitance both before and after any testing by short circuiting and grounding the equipment and cables under test. Consult manufacturer's bulletins and pertinent references to determine, prior to such shorting or grounding, if a specified "discharge" or "bleed" or "grounding" resistor should be used in the shorting/grounding circuit to limit the magnitude of the discharge current.

(5) Generally, there is no fire hazard in the normal use of a megohmmeter. There is, however, a hazard when testing equipment located in inflammable or explosive atmospheres. Slight sparking may be encountered when attaching test leads to equipment in which the capacitance has not been completely discharged or when discharging capacitance following a test. It is therefore suggested that use of a megohmmeter in an explosive atmosphere

be avoided if at all possible. If however testing must be conducted in an explosive atmosphere, then it is suggested that test leads not be disconnected for at least 30 to 60 seconds following a test, so as to allow time for capacitance discharge.

(6) Do not use a megohmmeter whose terminal operating voltage exceeds that which is safe to apply to the equipment under test.

d. To take a spot insulation reading, connect the megohmmeter across the insulation to be tested and operate it for a short, specific timed period (60 seconds usually is recommended). Bear in mind also that temperature and humidity, as well as the condition of your insulation, affect your reading. Your very first spot reading on equipment, with no prior test, can be only a rough guide as to how "good" or "bad" the insulation is. By taking readings periodically and recording them, you have a better basis of judging the actual insulation condition. Any persistent downward trend is usually fair warning of trouble ahead, even though the readings may be higher than the suggested minimum safe values. Equally true, as long as your periodic readings are consistent, they may be OK, even though lower than the recommended minimum values. You should make these periodic tests in the same way each time, with the same test connections and with the same test voltage applied for the same length of time. Table 4-3 includes some general observations about how you can interpret periodic insulation resistance tests and what you should do with the results.

e. Another insulation test method is the time resistance method. It is fairly independent of temperature and often can give you conclusive information without records of past tests. You simply take successive readings at specific times and note the differences in readings. Tests by this method are sometimes referred to as absorption tests. Test voltages applied are the same as those for the spot reading test. Note that good insulation shows a continual increase in resistance over a period of time. If the insulation contains much moisture or contaminants' the absorption effect is masked by a high leakage current which stays at a fairly constant value-keeping the resistance reading low. The time resistance test is of value also because it is independent of equipment size. The increase in resistance for clean and dry insulation occurs in the same manner whether a generator is large or small. You can therefore compare several generators and establish standards for new ones, regardless of their kW ratings.

f. The ratio of two time resistance readings is called a Dielectric Absorption Ratio. It is useful in recording information about insulation. If the ratio is a lo-minute reading divided by a 1-minute reading, the value is called the Polarization Index. Table 4-4 gives values of the ratio and corresponding relative conditions of the insulation that they indicate.

Table 4-3. Interpreting insulation resistance test results.

TEST RESULTS	
Condition	What to Do
1. Fair to high values and well-maintained	No cause for concern
2. Fair to high values, but showing a constant tendency towards lower values	Locate and remedy the cause and check the downward trend
3. Low but well-maintained	Condition is probably all right, but cause of low values should be checked
4. So low as to be unsafe	Clean, dry out or otherwise raise the values before placing equipment in service (Test wet equipment while drying out)
5. Fair or high values, previously well-maintained but showing sudden lowering	Make tests at frequent intervals until the cause of low values is located and remedied; or until the values have become steady at a lower level but safe for operation; or until values become so low that it is unsafe to keep the equipment in operation

*Table 4-4. Condition of insulation indicated by dielectric absorption ratios. ***

Insulation Condition	60/30-Second Ratio	10/1-Minute Ratio Polarization Index
Dangerous	—	Less than 1
Questionable	1.0 to 1.25	1.0 to 2
Good	1.4 to 1.6	2 to 4
Excellent	Above 1.6**	Above 4**

* These values must be considered tentative and relative; subject to experience with the time resistance method over a period of time.

** In some cases with motors, values approximately 20 percent higher than shown here indicate a dry brittle winding which will fail under shock conditions or during starts. For preventive maintenance, the motor winding should be cleared, treated and dried to restore winding flexibility.

CHAPTER 5

SWITCHGEAR

5-1. Switchgear definition.

Switchgear is a general term covering switching and interrupting devices that control, meter and protect the flow of electric power. The component parts include circuit breakers, instrument transformers, transfer switches, voltage regulators, instruments, and protective relays and devices. Switchgear includes associated interconnections and supporting or enclosing structures. The various configurations range in size from a single panel to an assembly of panels and enclosures (see fig 5-1). Figure 5-2 contains a diagram of typical switchgear control circuitry. Switchgear subdivides large blocks of electric power and performs the following missions:

a. Distributes incoming power between technical and non-technical loads.

b. Isolates the various loads.

c. Controls auxiliary power sources.

d. Provides the means to determine the quality and status of electric power.

e. Protects the generation and distribution systems.

5-2. Types of switchgear.

Voltage classification. Low voltage and medium voltage switchgear equipment are used in auxiliary power generation systems. Switchgear at military installations is usually in a grounded, metal enclosure (see fig 5-l). Per the Institute of Electrical and Electronics Engineers (IEEE), equipment rated up to 1000 volts AC is classed as low voltage. Equipment equal to or greater than 1000 volts but less than 100,000 volts AC is classed as medium voltage.

a. *Low voltage.* Major elements of low voltage switchgear are circuit breakers, potential transformers, current transformers, and control circuits, refer to paragraph 5-3. Related elements of the switchgear include the service entrance conductor, main box, switches, indicator lights, and instruments. The service entrance conductor and main bus (sized as required) are typical heavy duty conductors used to carry heavy current loads.

b. *Medium voltage.* Medium voltage switchgear consists of major and related elements as in low voltage switchgear. Refer to paragraph 5-4 for details. Construction of circuit breakers employed in the two types of switchgear and the methods to accomplish breaker tripping are the primary differences. The service entrance conductors and main

bus are typical heavy-duty conductors rated for use between 601 volts AC and 38,000 volts AC, as required.

5-3. Low voltage elements.

a. *Circuit breakers.* Either molded-case or air circuit breakers are used with low voltage switchgear. Usually the air circuit breakers have draw-out construction. This feature permits removal of an individual breaker from the switchgear enclosure for inspection or maintenance without de-energizing the main bus.

(1) *Air circuit breakers.* Air circuit breakers are usually used for heavy-duty, low voltage applications. Heavy-duty circuit breakers are capable of handling higher power loads than molded-case units and have higher current-interrupting capacity. Air circuit breakers feature actuation of contacts by stored energy which is either electrically or manually applied. Accordingly, the mechanism is powered to be put in a position where stored energy can be released to close or open the contacts very quickly. Closing or tripping action is applied manually (by hand or foot power) or electrically (where a solenoid provides mechanical force). The mechanical force may be applied magnetically. Air circuit breakers contain power sensor overcurrent trip devices that detect an overcurrent to the load and initiate tripping or opening of the circuit breaker.

(a) Manual circuit breakers employ spring-operated, stored-energy mechanisms for operation. Release of the energy results in quick operation of the mechanism to open or close the contacts. Operating speed is not dependent on the speed or force used by the operator to store the energy.

(b) Fast and positive action prevents unnecessary arcing between the movable and stationary contacts. This results in longer contact and breaker life.

(c) Manual stored-energy circuit breakers have springs which are charged (refer to the glossary) by operation of the insulated handle. The charging action energizes the spring prior to closing or opening of the circuit breaker. The spring, when fully charged, contains enough stored energy to provide at least one closing and one opening of the circuit breaker. The charged spring provides quick and positive operation of the circuit breaker. Part of the stored energy, which is released during closing, may be used to charge the opening springs.

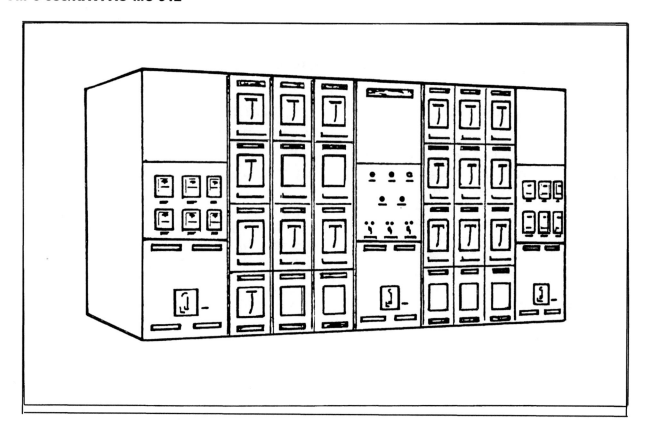

Figure 5-l. Typical arrangement of metal enclosed switchgear.

(d) Some manual breakers require several up-down strokes to fully charge. The springs are released on the final downward stroke. In either of the manual units, there is no motion of the contacts until the springs are released.

(e) Electrical quick-make/quick-break breakers are operated by a motor or solenoid. In small units, a solenoid is used to conserve space. In large sizes, an AC/DC motor is used to keep control-power requirements low (4 amps at 230 volts).

(f) When the solenoid is energized, the solenoid charges the closing springs and drives the mechanism past the central/neutral point in one continuous motion. Motor-operated mechanisms automatically charge the closing springs to a predetermined level. When a signal to close is delivered, the springs are released and the breaker contacts are closed. The motor or solenoid does not aid in the closing stroke; the springs supply all the closing power. There is sufficient stored-energy to close the contacts under short-circuit conditions. Energy for opening the contacts is stored during the closing action.

(g) A second set of springs opens the contacts when the breaker receives a trip impulse or signal. The breaker can be operated manually for maintenance by a detachable handle.

(h) Circuit breakers usually have two or three sets of contacts: main; arcing; and intermedi-

ate. Arcing and intermediate contacts are adjusted to open after the main contacts open to reduce burning or pitting of the main contacts.

(i) A typical power sensor for an air circuit breaker precisely controls the breaker opening time in response to a specified level of fault current. Most units function as overcurrent trip devices and consist of a solenoid tripper and solid-state components. The solid-state components are part of the power sensor and provide precise and sensitive trip signals.

(2) *Molded-case circuit breakers.* Low current and low energy power circuits are usually controlled by molded-case circuit breakers. The trip elements act directly to release the breaker latch when the current exceeds the calibrated current magnitude. Typical time-current characteristic curves for molded-case circuit breakers are shown in figure 5-3.

(a) Thermal-magnetic circuit breakers have a thermal bi-metallic element for an inverse time-current relationship to protect against sustained overloads. This type also has an instantaneous magnetic trip element for short-circuit protection.

(b) Magnetic trip-only circuit breakers have no thermal elements. This type has a magnetic tripping arrangement to trip instantaneously, with no purposely introduced time delay, at currents equal to, or above, the trip setting. These are used only for

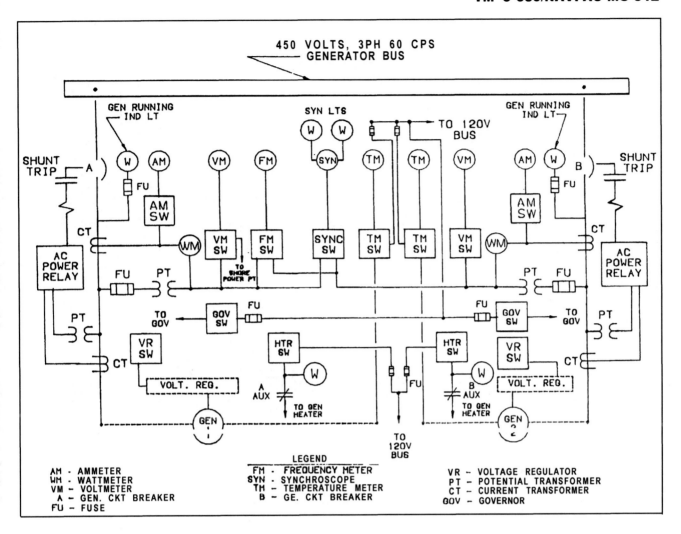

Figure 5-2. Typical switchgear control circuitry, one-line diagram.

short-circuit protection of motor branch circuits where motor overload or running protection is provided by other elements.

(c) Non-automatic circuit interrupters have no automatic overload or short circuit trip elements. These are used for manual switching and isolation. Other devices must be provided for short circuit and overload protection.

b. Potential transformers. A potential transformer (PT) is an accurately wound, low voltage loss instrument transformer having a fixed primary to secondary "step down" voltage ratio. The PT is mounted in the high voltage enclosure and only the low voltage leads from the secondary winding are brought out to the metering and control panel. The PT isolates the high voltage primary from the metering and control panel and from personnel. The step down ratio produces about 120 VAC across the secondary when rated voltage is applied to the primary. This permits the use of standard low voltage meters (120 VAC full scale) for all high voltage circuit metering and control.

(1) Ratings. A PT is rated for the primary voltage along with the turns (step down) ratio to secure 120 VAC across the secondary.

(2) Application. The primary of potential transformers is connected either line-to-line or line-to-neutral, and the current that flows through this winding produces a flux in the core. Since the core links the primary and secondary windings, a voltage is induced in the secondary circuit (see fig 5-4). The ratio of primary to secondary voltage is in proportion to the number of turns in the primary and secondary windings. This proportion produces 120 volts at the secondary terminals when rated voltage is applied to the primary.

(3) Dot convention. A dot convention is used in figure 5-5. The dot convention makes use of a large dot placed at one end of each of the two coils which are mutually coupled. A current entering the dotted terminal of one coil produces an open-circuit voltage between the terminals of the second coil. The voltage measured with a positive voltage reference at the dotted terminal of the second coil.

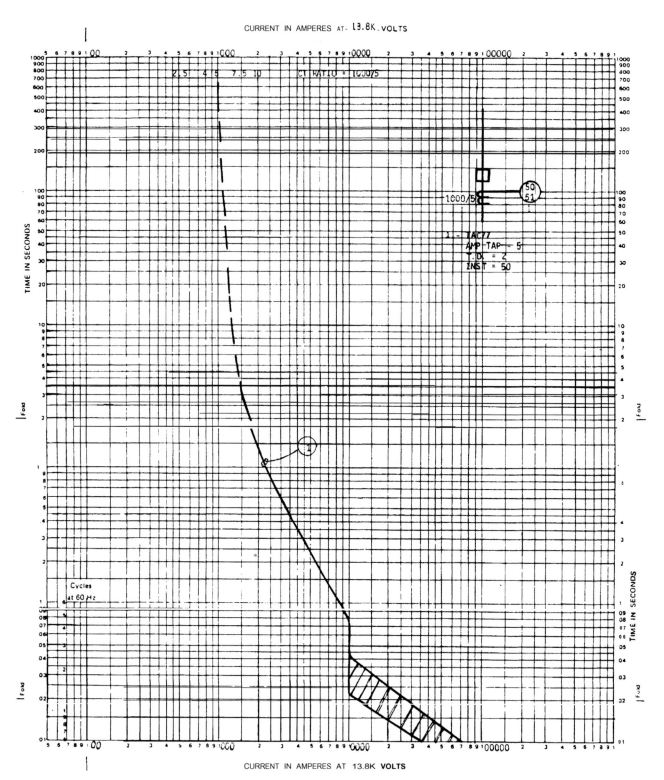

Figure 5-3. Typical time-current characteristic curve.

c. Current transformers. A current transformer (CT) is an instrument transformer having low losses whose purpose is to provide a fixed primary to secondary step down current ratio. The primary to secondary current ratio is in inverse proportion to the primary to secondary turns ratio. The secondary winding thus has multiple turns. The CT is usually either a toroid (doughnut) winding with a primary conductor wire passing through the "hole", or a section of bus bar (primary) around which is wound the secondary. The bus bar CT is inserted into the bus being measured. The CT ratio is selected to result in a five ampere secondary current when primary rated current is flowing (see fig 5-4).

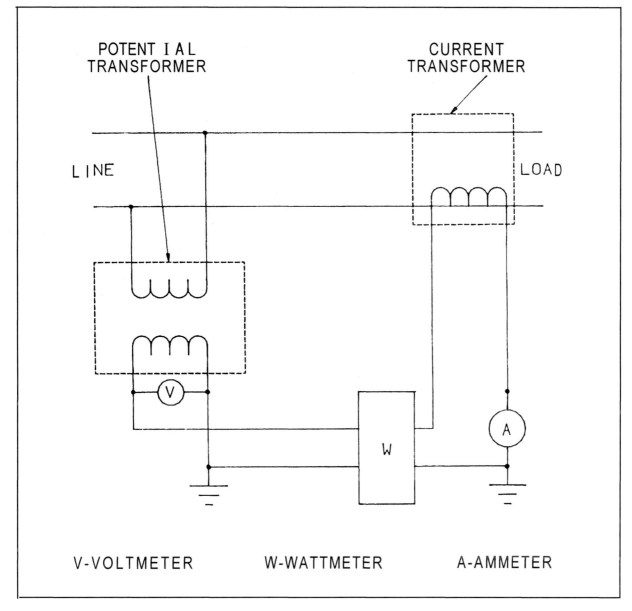

POTENTIAL
TRANSFORMER

CURRENT
TRANSFORMER

LINE

LOAD

W

V-VOLTMETER   W-WATTMETER   A-AMMETER

Figure 5-4. Instrument transformers, typical applications.

(1) *Ratings.* Toroidal CTs are rated for the size of the primary conductor diameter to be surrounded and the primary to secondary current (5A) ratio. Bus bar type CTs are rated for the size of bus bar, primary voltage and the primary to secondary current 5A) ratio.

(2) *Application.* The primary of a CT is either the line conductor or a section of the line bus. The secondary current, up to 5A, is directly proportional to the line current. The ratio of the primary to secondary current is inversely proportional to the ratio of the primary turns to secondary turns.

(3) *Safety.* A CT, in stepping down the current, also steps up voltage. The voltage across the secondary is at a dangerously high level when the primary is energized. The secondary of a CT must either be shorted or connected into the closed metering cir-

cuit. Never open a CT secondary while the primary circuit is energized.

d. Polarities. When connection secondaries of PTs and Cts to metering circuits the correct polarities of all leads and connections must be in accordance with the metering circuit design and the devices connected. Wrong polarity connections will give false readings and result in inaccurate data, damage and injury. All conductors and terminations should carry identification that matches schematics, diagrams and plans used for construction and maintenance.

e. Control circuits. Switchgear control circuits provide control power for the starting circuit of the prime movers and the closing and tripping of the switchgear circuit breakers. Additionally, the control circuits provide control power to operate the

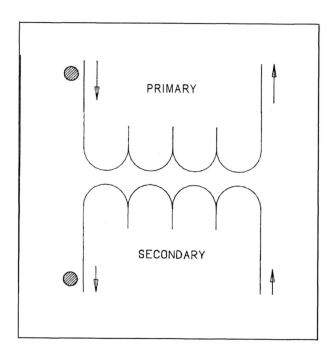

Figure 5-5. Current flow in instrument transformers. "Polarity" marks show instantaneous flows.

various relays and indicating lights associated with the control circuitry. The control circuits are classified as either AC or DC.

(1) *AC control circuits.* AC control circuits usually derive their power from the source side of the circuit breaker being controlled. This procedure applies to main incoming line circuit breakers, generator circuit breakers, and feeder circuit breakers (see fig 5-6). Depending on the system voltage, the control power can be taken directly from the main bus since it can be connected through a control power transformer.

(2) Tie *breaker control circuits.* In systems using a tie breaker, the control power for the tie breaker and the feeder breakers is supplied through a throw-over scheme so control power is available if either side of the tie breaker is energized (see fig 5-7). In applications that require synchronizing circuitry, the running and incoming control buses are usually supplied via the potential transformers. The transformer primaries are connected to both the line side and the load side of the circuit breakers that are used for synchronizing. The transformer

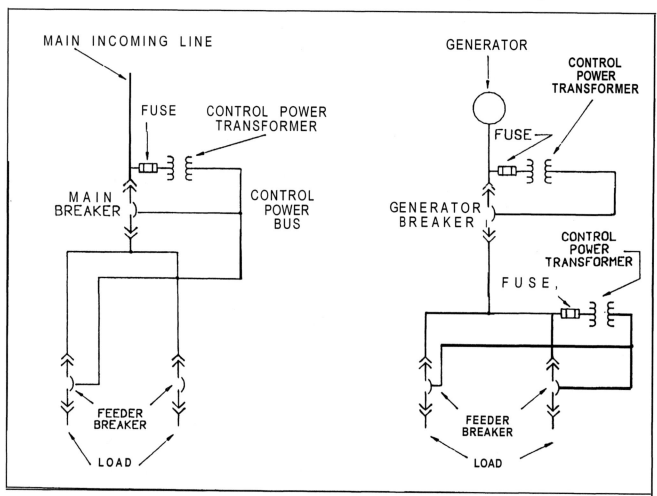

Figure 5-6. AC control circuits.

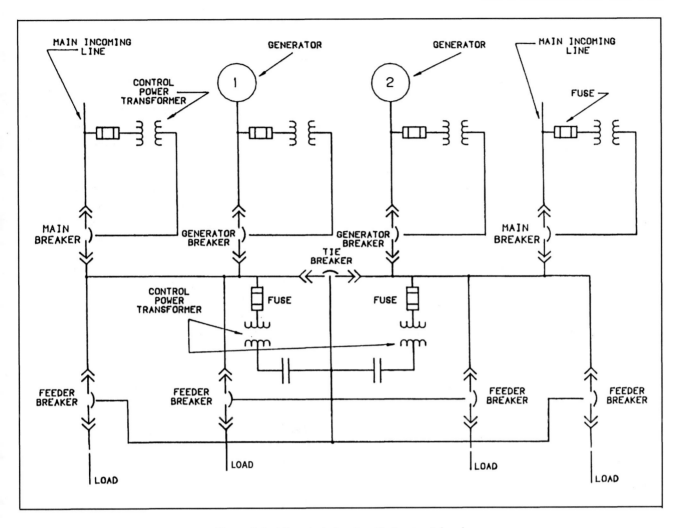

Figure 5-7. AC control circuits with tie circuit breaker.

secondaries are connected to the proper control bus through contacts on the synchronizing switch, or through contacts on certain auxiliary relays. The synchronizing switch would be used for manual operation and the auxiliary relay would be used when automatic synchronizing is provided.

(3) *DC control circuits.* DC control circuits derive their power from a battery source consisting of a bank of batteries and a battery charger that maintains the batteries at the proper charge. The battery bank can be rated at various levels ranging between 24 volts and 125 volts DC. Those circuits that require a source of control power completely independent of the power system are connected to the DC control bus. Examples of these are the prime mover starting circuits, and in some cases, the trip circuits for the circuit breakers when devices, other than the direct-acting overcurrent trip devices, are used. Also, the closing circuits for the circuit breakers are sometimes connected to the DC control bus.

f. Service practices. Service practices for low voltage switchgear consist of a complete maintenance

program that is built around equipment and system records and visual inspections. The program is described in the manufacturer's literature furnished with the components. If a problem develops, the user should perform general troubleshooting procedures. The program includes appropriate analysis of the records.

(1) *Record keeping.* Equipment and system log sheets are important and necessary functions of record keeping. The log sheets must be specifically developed to suit individual application (i.e., auxiliary use).

(2) *Troubleshooting.* Perform troubleshooting procedures when abnormal operation of the system or equipment is observed. Maintenance personnel must then refer to records for interpretation and comparison of performance data (i.e., log sheets). Comparisons of operation should be made under equal or closely similar conditions of load and ambient temperature. The general scheme for troubleshooting is outlined in the following paragraphs and troubleshooting table.

(a) Use recognized industrial practices as the general guide for servicing and refer to manufacturer's literature.

(b) The user should refer to manufacturer's literature for specific information on individual circuit breakers.

(c) General service information for circuit breakers includes the following safety requirements. Do not work on an energized breaker. Do not work on any part of a breaker with test couplers engaged. Test couplers connect the breaker to the control circuit during testing. Spring-charged breaker mechanisms shall be serviced only by personnel experienced in releasing the spring load in a controlled manner. Make operational tests and checks on a breaker after maintenance, before it is returned to service. Do not work on a spring-charged circuit breaker when it is in the charged position.

(d) Switchgear needs exercise. If the circuit breaker remains idle, either open or closed, for six months or more, it should be opened and closed

several times during the period, preferably under load. If the breaker is operated by a relay or a switch, it should be so operated at this time.

(e) Service for molded-case circuit breakers consists of the following procedures. Inspect connections for signs of arcing or overheating. Replace faulty connectors and tighten all connections. Clean the connecting surfaces. Perform overload tripping tests. Verify automatic opening of breaker. Verify that the magnetic tripping feature is operating. Perform circuit breaker overload tripping tests. Proper action of the breaker tripping components is verified by selecting a percentage of breaker current rating (such as 300%) for testing. This overload is applied separately to each pole of the breaker to determine how it will affect automatic opening of the breaker. Refer to manufacturer's test information. Turn the breaker on and off several times to verify satisfactory mechanical operation.

(f) Service for air circuit breakers consists of the following procedure (see fig 5-8). Install the safety pin to restrain the closing spring force. With

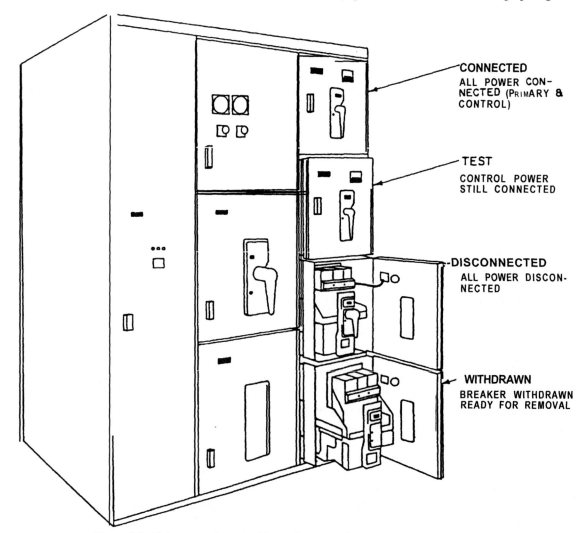

CONNECTED
ALL POWER CON-
NECTED (PRIMARY &
CONTROL)

TEST
CONTROL POWER
STILL CONNECTED

DISCONNECTED
ALL POWER DISCON-
NECTED

WITHDRAWN
BREAKER WITHDRAWN
READY FOR REMOVAL

Figure 5-8. Maintenance for typical low voltage switchgear with air circuit breakers.

the pin in place, the contacts will close slowly when the breaker is manually operated. Inspect connections for signs of arcing or overheating. Replace faulty connectors and tighten all connections. Clean the connecting surfaces. An infrared (IR) survey is a recommended inspection procedure. The IR survey should be performed when the circuit breaker is under load and closed to detect overheating of connections. Perform general troubleshooting of the breaker (refer to the following table) if a problem develops. If the trouble cannot be corrected, refer to the manufacturer's literature for specific information on individual breakers. Instrument transformers require no care other than keeping them dry and clean. Refer to manufacturer's literature if specific information is required. Information related to control circuit components is provided in paragraph 5-3e of this chapter.

Table 5-l. Low voltage circuit breaker troubleshooting.

Note

Refer to manufacturer's literature for specific information on individual circuit breakers.

Cause	Remedy
OVERHEATING	
Contacts not aligned	Adjust contacts
Contacts dirty, greasy, or coated with dark film	Clean contacts
Contacts badly burned or pitted	Replace contacts
Current-carrying surfaces dirty	Clean surfaces of current-carrying parts
Corrosive atmosphere	Relocate or provide adequate enclosure
Insufficient bus or cable capacity	Increase capacity of bus or cable
Bolts and nuts at terminal connections not tight	Tighten, but do not exceed, elastic limit of bolts or fittings
Current in excess of breaker rating	Check breaker applications or modify circuit by decreasing load
Inductive heating	Correct bus or cable arrangement
FAILURE TO TRIP	
Travel of tripping device does not provide positive release of tripping latch	Adjust or replace tripping device
Worn or damaged trip unit parts	Replace trip unit
Mechanical binding in overcurrent trip device	Correct binding condition or replace overcurrent trip device
Electrical connectors for power sensor loose or open	Tighten, connect, or replace electrical connectors
Loose or broken power sensor connections	Tighten or re-connect tap coil tap connections

Table 5-l. Low voltage circuit breaker troubleshooting-Continued

Note

Refer to manufacturer's literature for specific information on individual circuit breakers.

Cause	Remedy
FALSE TRIPPING	
Overcurrent pick-up too low	Check application of overcurrent trip device
Overcurrent time setting too short	Check application of overcurrent trip device
Mechanical binding in over-condition current trip device	Correct binding or replace overcurrent trip device
Captive thumbscrew on power sensor loose. Fail safe circuitry reverts characteristics to minimum setting and maximum time delay	Adjust power sensor. Tighten thumbscrew on desired setting
Ground sensor coil improperly connected	Check polarity of connections to coil. Check continuity of shield and conductors connecting the external ground sensor coil
FAILURE TO CLOSE AND LATCH	
Binding in attachments preventing resetting of latch	Realign and adjust attachments
Latch out of adjustment	Adjust latch
Latch return spring too weak or broken	Replace spring
Hardened or gummy lubricant	Clean bearing and latch surfaces
Safety pin left in push rod	Remove safety pin
Motor burned out	Replace motor
Faulty control circuit component	Replace or adjust faulty device
BURNED MAIN CONTACTS	
Improper contact sequence (main contacts not sufficiently parted when arcing contacts part)	Increase arcing contact wipe Adjust contact opening sequence Refer to opening. Refer to manufacturer's literature for contact maintenance and adjustment information. Also refer to paragraph 5-3a(l)(.g)
Short-circuit current level above interrupting rating of breaker	Requires system study and possible replacement with breaker having adequate interrupting capacity

5-4. Medium voltage elements.

a. Circuit breakers. Medium voltage switchgear uses oil, air-blast, or vacuum circuit breakers. Usually the circuit breakers have draw-out construction to permit removal of an individual breaker from the enclosure for inspection or maintenance without de-energizing the main bus. All of these circuit breakers can quickly interrupt and extinguish the electric arc that occurs between breaker contacts when the contacts are separated.

(1) *Oil circuit breakers.* When the contacts are separated in oil, the interrupted voltage and current can be greater as compared to contact separation in air at room temperature.

(a) Arc interruption is better in oil than air because the dielectric strength of oil is much greater than air. Also, the arc generates hydrogen gas from the oil (see fig 5-9). The gas is superior to air as a cooling medium.

(b) Usually the contacts and the arc are enclosed in a fiber arcing chamber, with exhaust ports on one side, to increase the capacity.

(2) *Air circuit breakers.* Arc extinction by high pressure air blast is another method of quickly interrupting and extinguishing electric arc. Cross-blast type breakers are usually used in medium voltage switchgear.

(a) A cross-blast breaker uses an arc chute with one splitter (insulating fin) that functions as an arc barrier (see fig 5-10).

(b) The arc is drawn between the upper and lower electrodes. During interruption, a blast of high-pressure air is directed across the arc pushing the arc against the splitter. The arc is broken at current zero and carried downstream.

(3) *Vacuum circuit breakers.* Vacuum arc interruption is the newest and quickest method of extinguishing an electric arc. This type of breaker (see figure 5-11) is oil-less, fireproof and nearly maintenance free. Service life is very long. Arc interruption is very rapid, usually in the first current zero. High dielectric strength of a small vacuum gap contributes to the rapid interruption of the arc. Short contact travel permits the mechanism to part the contacts much faster than for oil breakers.

(4) *Warning.* Mechanical indication of "open" may not be true. Always make sure no voltage exists on load/line side before performing any work.

b. *Potential transformers.* A potential transformer (PT) is an accurately wound, low voltage-loss instrument transformer having a fixed primary to secondary "step down" voltage ratio. The PT is mounted in the high voltage enclosure and only the low voltage leads from the secondary winding are

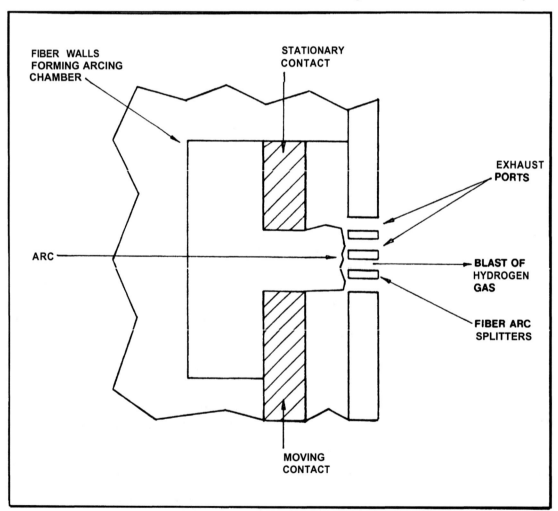

FIBER WALLS FORMING ARCING CHAMBER

STATIONARY CONTACT

EXHAUST PORTS

ARC

BLAST OF HYDROGEN GAS

FIBER ARC SPLITTERS

MOVING CONTACT

Figure 5-9. Arc interruption in oil, diagram.

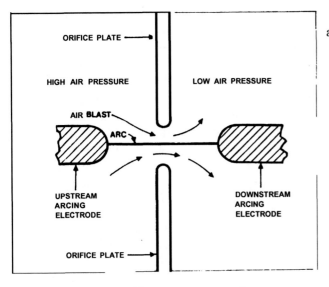

Figure 5-10. Air blast arc interrupter, diagram.

brought out to the metering and control panel. The PT isolates the high voltage primary from the metering and control panel and from personnel. The step down ratio produces about 120 VAC across the secondary when rated voltage is applied to the primary. This permits the use of standard low voltage meters (120 VAC full scale) for all high voltage circuit metering and control.

(1) *Ratings.* Potential transformers are usually rated at 120 volts in the secondary circuit.

(2) *Application.* Refer to paragraph 5-3*b*(2) for application information.

c. *Current transformers.* A Current Transformer (CT) is an instrument transformer having low losses whose purpose is to provide a fixed primary to secondary step down current ratio. The primary to secondary current ratio is in inverse proportion to the primary to secondary turns ratio. The secondary winding thus has multiple turns. The CT is usually either a toroid (doughnut) winding with primary conductor wire passing through the "hole" or a unit section of bus bar (primary), around which is wound the secondary, inserted into the bus run. The CT ratio is selected to result in a five ampere secondary current when primary rated current is flowing.

(1) *Ratings.* Current transformers are usually rated at 5 amperes in the secondary circuit.

(2) *Application.* Refer to paragraph 5-3*c*(2) application information.

d. *Control circuits.* Switchgear control circuits for medium voltage are functionally similar to those used for low voltage systems. The control circuits are similarly classified as either AC or DC.

(1) *AC control circuits.* Refer to the description provided in paragraph 5-3*e*(1).

(2) *DC control circuits.* Refer to the description provided in paragraph 5-3*e*(3).

e. *Service practices.* Service practices for medium voltage switchgear consist of a complete mainte-

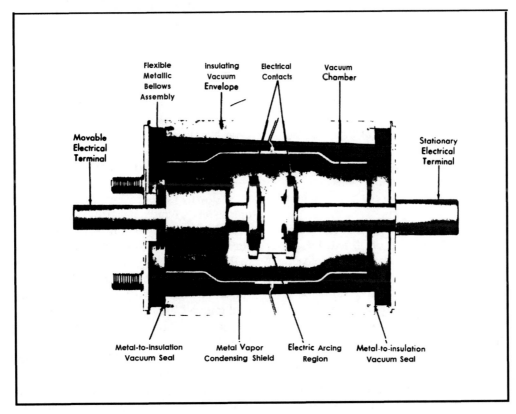

Figure 5-11. Cross sectional view of vacuum arc interrupter:

nance program that is built around equipment, system records, and visual inspections. The program is described in the manufacturer's literature furnished with the components. If a problem develops, the user should perform general troubleshooting procedures. The program includes appropriate analysis of the records.

(1) Record *keeping.* Equipment and system log sheets are important and necessary functions of record keeping. The log sheets must be specifically developed to suit individual applications (i.e., auxiliary use).

(2) *Troubleshooting.* Perform troubleshooting procedures when abnormal operation of the system or equipment is observed. Maintenance personnel must then refer to records for interpretation and comparison of performance data (i.e., log sheets). Comparisons of operation should be made under equal or closely similar conditions of load and ambient temperature. The general scheme for troubleshooting is outlined in the following paragraphs.

(a) Use recognized industrial practices as the general guide for servicing and refer to manufacturer's literature.

(b) The user should refer to manufacturer's literature for specific information on individual circuit breakers.

(c) General service information for circuit breakers includes the following safety requirements. Do not work on an energized breaker. Do not work on any part of a breaker with the test couplers engaged. Test couplers connect the breaker to the control circuit during testing. Maintenance closing devices for switchgear are not suitable for closing in on a live system. Speed in closing is as important as speed in opening. A wrench or other maintenance tool is not fast enough. Before working on the switchgear enclosure, remove all draw-out devices such as circuit breakers and instrument transformers. Do not lay tools down on the equipment while working on it. It is too easy to forget a tool when closing an enclosure.

(d) Switchgear needs exercise. If the circuit breaker remains idle, either open or closed, for six months or more, it should be opened and closed several times during the period, preferably under load. If the breaker is operated by a relay or a switch, it too should be operated at this time.

(e) Service circuit breakers using insulating liquid require special handling. Elevate the breaker on an inspection rack and untank it to expose the contacts. The insulating liquid usually used in circuit breakers is mineral oil. Equipment using liquids containing polychlorinated biphenyls (PCBs) may still be in use. Since PCBs are carcinogenic and not biodegradable, some restrictions to their use apply. Silicone insulating liquid can be used as substitute for PCBs when authorized by the Base engineer. Special handling is required if PCBs are used in any equipment. Refer to 40 CFR 761 for PCB details. PCBs are powerful solvents. Handling and disposal information and special gloves are required. Check condition, alignment, and adjustment of contacts. Verify that contacts surfaces bear with firm, even pressure. Use a fine file to dress rough contacts; replace pitted or burned contacts. Wipe clean all parts normally immersed in liquid, remove traces of carbon that remain after the liquid has drained. Inspect insulating parts for cracks, or other damage requiring replacement. Test the dielectric strength of the liquid, using a 0.1 inch gap with 1.1 inch diameter disk terminals. If strength is less than 22 kV, remove and filter or replace with new liquid having a dielectric strength of at least 26 kV. Filter the liquid whenever inspection shows excessive carbon, even if its dielectric strength is satisfactory, because the carbon will deposit on insulating surfaces decreasing the insulation strength. Liquid samples should be taken in a large-mouthed glass bottle that has been cleaned and dried with benzene. Use a cork stopper with this bottle. Draw test samples from the bottom of the tank after the liquid has settled. The samples should be from the tank proper and not from the valve or drain pipe. Periodically remove the liquid from the tank and wipe the inside of the tank, the tank linings, and barriers to remove carbon. Inspect breaker and operating mechanisms for loose hardware and missing or broken cotter pins, retaining rings, etc. Check adjustments and readjust when necessary (refer to the manufacturer's instruction book). Clean operating mechanism and lubricate as for air-magnetic type breakers (refer to the manufacturer's instruction book). Before replacing the tank, operate breaker slowly with maintenance closing device to verify there is no friction or binding to prevent or slow down its operation; then, check the electrical operation. Avoid operating the breaker any more than is necessary when testing it without liquid in the tank. It is designed to operate in liquid and mechanical damage can result from excessive operation without it. When replacing the tank, fill to the correct level with liquid, be sure the gaskets are undamaged and the tank nuts and flange nuts on gauges and valves are tightened properly to prevent leakage.

(f) Service air-blast type circuit breakers. Circuit breakers should be serviced (tested, exercised, and calibrated) at intervals not to exceed two years (refer to AR 420-43). Withdraw the breaker from its housing for maintenance. Circuit breakers

are designed to perform up to 5000 and 3000 operations for 1200 ampere or 200 ampere breakers, respectively, without major overhaul. More frequent servicing may be necessary if operating conditions are severe. Inspection and servicing should be performed after every fault clearing operation. Refer to instructions provided by the manufacturer. Wipe insulating parts, including bushings and the inside of box barriers; clean off smoke and dust. Repair moderate damage to bushing insulation by sanding smooth and refinishing with a clear insulating varnish. Inspect alignment and condition of movable and stationary contacts. Check their adjustment as described in the manufacturer's instruction book. To check alignment, close the breaker with pieces of tissue and carbon paper between the contacts and examine the impression. Do not file butt-type contacts. Contacts which have been roughened in service may carry current as well as smooth contacts. Remove large projections or "bubbles" caused by unusual arcing, by filing. When filing to touch up, keep the contacts in their original design; that is, if the contact is a line type, keep the area of contact linear, and if ball or point-type, keep the ball or points shaped out. Check arc chutes for damage. Replace damaged parts. When arc chutes are removed, blow out dust and loose particles. Clean silver-plated breaker primary disconnecting devices with alcohol or silver polish (refer to the manufacturer's instruction book). Lubricate devices by applying a thin film of approved grease. Inspect breaker operating mechanism for loose hardware and missing or broken cotter pins, retaining rings, etc. Examine cam, latch and roller surfaces for damage or excessive wear. Clean and relubricate operating mechanism (refer to the manufacturer's instruction book). Lubricate pins and bearings not disassembled. Lubricate the ground or polished surfaces of cams, rollers, latches and props, and of pins and bearings that are removed for cleaning. Check breaker operating mechanism adjustments and readjust as described in the manufacturer's instruction book. If adjustments cannot be made within specified tolerances, excessive wear and need for a complete overhaul is indicated. Check control device for freedom of operation. Replace contacts when badly worn or burned. Inspect breaker control wiring for tightness of connections. After the breaker has been serviced, operate it slowly with closing device to check absence of binding or friction and check that contacts move to the fully-opened and fully-closed positions. Check electrical operation using either the test cabinet or test couplers.

(g) Service vacuum circuit breakers. This breaker has primary contacts enclosed in vacuum containers (flasks), and direct inspection or replacement is not possible. The operating mechanism is similar to that used in other medium voltage circuit breakers, and the general outlines are the same for maintenance work. The enclosures are similar. Figure 5-11 shows a breaker with the primary electrical contacts exposed. The stationary contact is solidly mounted; the moving contact is mounted in the enclosure with a bellows seal. Contact erosion is measured by the change in external shaft positions after a period of use. Consult the manufacturer's instruction book. High voltage applied during testing may produce X-ray emission. Personnel performing a hi-pot test must stay behind a protective shield during testing. Condition of the vacuum is checked by a hi-pot test applied every maintenance period. Consult manufacturer's instruction book for test procedures. The contacts in a vacuum circuit breaker cannot be cleaned, repaired or adjusted. The vacuum bottle is usually replaced if the test indicates a fault.

5-5. Transfer switches.

During actual or threatened power failure, transfer switches are actuated to transfer critical electrical load circuits from the normal source of power to the auxiliary (emergency) power source. When normal power is restored, the transfer switches either automatically retransfer their load circuits to the normal supply or must be transferred manually. Voltage and frequency-sensing relays are provided to monitor each phase of the normal supply. The relays initiate load transfer when there is a change in voltage or frequency in any phase outside of predetermined limits. Additionally, the relays initiate retransfer of the load to the normal source as soon as voltage is restored in all the phases beyond the predetermined pick-up value of the relay. A transfer switch obtains its operating current from the source to which the load is being transferred.

a. Types of transfer switches. There are two types of transfer switches: electrically operated or manually operated. Electrically operated transfer switches also come with an optional bypass function.

(1) *Electrically operated.* An electrically operated switch obtains its operating current from the source to which the load is being transferred. A separate voltage supply is used in some systems. Electrically operated switches consist of three functional elements: main contacts to connect and disconnect the load to and from the sources of power; sensing circuits to constantly monitor the condition of the power source and provide the information necessary for switch and related circuit operation; and transfer mechanism to make the transfer from source to source.

(a) Circuit breaker type. Circuit breaker transfer switches are mechanically held devices using two circuit breakers. Usually the breaker handles are operated by a transfer mechanism which provides double-throw switching action connecting one circuit terminal to either of two others. The transfer mechanism is operated electrically by a unidirectional gear motor (motor and integral speed-reducing gearbox) or by dual motor operators with all parts in positive contact at all times. These switches can also be operated manually and have provisions for disengaging the generator when necessary.

(b) Neutral position. Some transfer switches have a neutral position. However, the switch is mechanically and electrically interlocked so that a neutral position is not possible during electrical operation. Also, load circuits cannot be connected by the switch to normal and emergency sources simultaneously whether the switch is operated electrically or manually.

(c) Contactor type. Contactor type transfer switches have mechanically or electrically held contactors with a command load bus. The switches are mechanically and electrically interlocked so that a neutral position is not possible under normal electrical operation. Additionally, the load circuits cannot be connected to normal and emergency sources simultaneously.

(2) Bypass function. An electrically operated transfer switch can be provided with a bypass function. The bypass function manually transfers the power around the automatic transfer switch. The electrically operated switch can then be tested, removed, and repaired. The bypass function may or may not cause a momentary interruption to the load depending upon the manufacturer. The bypass is purely a manual function, therefore, if the source to which the bypass is connected fails the bypass must be manually transferred to the alternate source. Bypass transfer switches are only used in the most critical applications where the load is operational continuously.

(3) Manually operated. Manual transfer switches are mechanically held devices using two circuit breakers operated by a handle. All parts are in positive contact at all times. The switch is mechanically interlocked; it is impossible for the load circuits to be connected to normal and emergency sources simultaneously. Manually operated transfer switches are available with single or dual operating handles. A common operating mechanism across the two breakers mechanically connects and operates the breakers.

b. Operation. Transfer switches have two operating modes: automatic and non-automatic.

(1) Automatic. Automatic transfer switches have voltage sensing relays for each phase. The sensing relays are connected to the normal power bus, behind the protecting devices.

(a) The transfer switch is connected to the normal power source under normal conditions. When the sensing relays detect a sustained drop in the voltage of the normal power source, the relays will automatically start the auxiliary generator. The transfer switch operates upon a sustained drop in voltage in any phase of the normal source (approximately a 30 percent drop and delay of about two seconds) to start the auxiliary generator.

(b) When voltage and frequency of the auxiliary generator are at rated values, and the normal power source is still below normal, the automatic control will transfer the load to the emergency source.

(c) Upon return of normal power to within 10 percent of rated voltage on all phases and after a preset time delay, the switch automatically transfers the load to the normal source. Usually the auxiliary generator will run unloaded for about five minutes after the transfer, before it shuts down. The controls automatically reset for the next emergency start.

(d) Usually the controls of a power transfer system have a test switch. This permits simulation of failure of the normal power source and test of transfer switch operation.

(e) Power transfer indicators are provided in most automatic transfer systems to indicate the currently used power source. Usually an amber light marked "Emergency Power" shows that the system is on emergency power when illuminated. A white light marked "Normal Power" shows that the system is receiving power from its normal source when illuminated.

(2) Nonautomatic. In nonautomatic operation, an operator is needed to manually transfer to or from the emergency power source. The operator can usually make the transfer without opening an enclosure. The transfer is usually based on instrument indications and is made by placing the transfer switch in the required emergency or normal position.

(a) Power transfer indicators are provided for the operator. An amber light (Emergency Power) shows that the system is on emergency power when illuminated. A white light (Normal Power) shows that the system is receiving power from its normal source when illuminated.

(b) The operator is usually provided with an override switch which bypasses the automatic transfer controls. This feature permits indefinite

connection of the emergency power source regardless of the condition of the normal power source.

c. Service practices. Service practices for transfer switches consist of a complete maintenance program that is built around records and visual inspections. The program includes appropriate analysis of these records.

(1) Record keeping. Equipment and system log sheets are important and necessary functions of record keeping. The log sheets must be specifically developed to suit auxiliary use.

(2) Troubleshooting. Use recognized industrial practices as the general guide for transfer switch and system troubleshooting. Troubleshooting of system circuits that are not performing according to specifications and to the required performance level should be accomplished as follows: refer to engineering data and drawings pertaining to the particular plant.

(a) The user should refer to manufacturer's literature for specific information on individual transfer switches.

(b) Perform general troubleshooting of the transfer switch if a problem develops. Refer to the manufacturer's literature for specific information. Usually, all control elements are renewable from the front of the switch without removing the switch from its enclosures and without removing the main power cables.

5-6. Regulators.

A voltage regulator maintains the terminal voltage of an alternator or generator at a predetermined value. Voltage is controlled by regulating the strength of the electromagnetic field produced in the alternator exciter. A voltage regulator automatically overcomes voltage drop within the alternator by changing field excitation automatically as it varies with the load.

a. Types of regulators. The types of voltage regulators are electromechanical, static voltage, and static exciter.

(1) *Electro-mechanical voltage regulators.* These regulators usually have a servo-control system with three principal elements.

(a) First is a voltage sensing device with a voltage regulating relay. The device monitors the output voltage and sends a signal to the control circuits.

(b) Second is an amplifying section with or without time delay, which amplifies the voltage signal.

(c) Third is a motor drive which responds to the signal by moving a tap changer or induction regulator in a direction to correct the voltage.

(2) *Static voltage regulators.* A static regulator usually has a static voltage sensor instead of a voltage-regulating relay.

(a) Operation. The voltage sensor output is applied to a solid-state or magnetic amplifier and a discriminator circuit. Signals are thereby provided for changing alternator output to raise or lower the voltage as required. The voltage zone between initiation of raising or lowering control action is called the voltage band. The band must be more than the minimum correction obtainable through the regulator or regulator hunting will occur.

(b) Accessories. Accessories include either thermal delay relays or a resistance capacitance network to provide time delay for load trend correction. Time delay retards the signal until accumulated time outside the voltage limit, less accumulated time inside the voltage limit, exceeds the time delay setting.

(3) *Static exciter regulators.* A static exciter regulator supplies the alternator field with DC voltage obtained from a three-phase, full wave bridge rectifier.

(a) Operation. A small part of the alternator's output goes to the regulator which meters the rectified DC voltage back to exciter's field windings. The rectified DC voltage produces a 60 cycle ripple. If the ripple gets into the field windings, an electrical discharge from windings to shaft can occur. A filter can be used to reduce ripple. The discharge is caused because copper in the field windings and the metal shaft act like the plates in a capacitor. This action may result in shaft and bearing pitting and eventual bearing failure. A static exciter is a manufactured subassembly, assembled and wired at the manufacturer's plant, usually using one or more silicon rectifiers to convert AC voltage to DC. The subassembly usually includes a regulator and a filter. Refer to the manufacturer's literature for test and adjustment details.

(b) Accessories. Accessories include either thermal delay relays or a resistance capacitance network to provide time delay for load trend correction (refer to para 5-6a(2)(b). A suppressor circuit or ripple filter is usually provided to bypass ripple to ground before it gets to the generator field.

b. Service practices. Service practices for voltage regulators consist of a complete maintenance program that is built around records and visual inspections. The program includes appropriate analysis of these records.

(1) *Record keeping.* Equipment and system log sheets are important and necessary functions of record keeping. The log sheets must be specifically developed to suit auxiliary use.

(2) *Troubleshooting.* Use recognized industrial practices as the general guide for servicing. Refer to manufacturer's literature for specific information on individual voltage regulators. Troubleshooting procedures include the following:

(a) Check voltage for compliance with manufacturer's specifications.

(b) Check for loose or insecure electrical connections.

(c) Check for correct setting, refer to manufacturer's literature.

(d) Check for unregulated voltage. Refer to manufacturer's literature.

(e) Check the enclosure. Should be weather tight.

(f) Check motor for proper operation and loose connections. Clean and lubricate as required. Refer to manufacturer's literature for details.

(g) Voltage regulators and associated equipment are normally mounted within switchgear equipment and are interconnected with different components. The proper operation and troubleshooting of voltage regulator equipment can depend on these different components. Perform the procedures in the following table:

Table 5-2. Switchgear equipment troubleshooting.

Note

Refer to manufacturer's literature for specific information on individual equipment.

Cause	Remedy
WATTHOUR METER INACCURATE	
Meter may be dirty or damaged	Install new meter, return faulty meter to repair depot for repair and calibration
Faulty wiring or connections	Inspect and repair as necessary
WATTHOUR METER FAILS TO REGISTER	
Blown potential transformer **fuse,** broken wires or other fault in connections	Renew blown fuses Check wiring and repair as required
Wedge or block accidently left at time of test or inspection	Remove wedge or block Verify that meter is in good operating condition
DAMAGED CONTROL, INSTRUMENT TRANSFER SWITCH, OR TEST BLOCKS	
Burned or pitted contacts	Dress or clean burned contacts or replace with new contacts if necessary
RELAYS FAILING TO TRIP BREAKERS	
Improper setting	Adjust setting to correspond with circuit conditions. Refer to manufacturer's instructions
Dirty, corroded or tarnished contacts	Clean contact with knife or tile Do not use emery cloth or sand-paper

Table 5-2. Switchgear equipment troubleshooting-Continued

Note

Refer to manufacturer's literature for specific information on individual equipment.

Cause	Remedy
RELAYS FAILING TO TRIP BREAKERS	
Contacts improperly adjusted	Adjust contacts. verify proper wipe action
Open or short circuit in relay connections	Check to verify that voltage is applied and that current is passing through relay in question
Improper application of target and holding coil	Verify proper tripping action of target and holding coils
Faulty or improperly adjusted timing devices	If timing device is of bellows or oil-film type, clean and adjust. if of induction-disk type, check for mechanical interference. Refer to manufacturer's literature
NOISES DUE TO VIBRATING PARTS	
Loose bolts or nuts permitting excessive vibration	Tighten to proper torque value
Loose laminations in cores of transformers, reactors, etc.	Tighten loose nuts or core clamps to proper torque value
CONNECTIONS OVERHEATING	
Increase of current due to overload conditions	Increase the carrying capacity (increase the number or size of conductors) Remove excess current from circuit
Connecting bolts and nuts not tight	Tighten ail bolts and nuts to proper torque value
FAILURE IN FUNCTION OF ALL INSTRUMENTS AND DEVICES HAVING POTENTIAL WINDINGS	
Loose nuts, binding screws or broken wire at terminals	Tighten all loose connections to proper torque value or repair broken wire circuits
Blown fuse in potential transformer circuit	Renew blown fuses
Open circuit in potential transformer primary or secondary circuits	Repair open circuit and check entire circuit for continuity and good condition
BREAKER FAILS TO TRIP	
Mechanism binding or sticking caused by lack of lubrication	Lubricate breaker mechanism; refer to manufacturer's instructions
Mechanism out of adjustment	Adjust all mechanical devices, (toggles, stops, buffers, opening springs, etc.) according to manufacturer's instructions
Failure of latching device	Examine surface of latch, replace latch if worn or corroded. Check latch wipe, adjust according to manufacturer's instructions
Damage trip coil	Replace damaged coil

Table 5-2. Switchgear equipment troubleshooting-Continued

Note

Refer to manufacturer's literature for specific information on individual equipment.

Cause	Remedy
BREAKER FAILS TO TRIP	
Blown fuse in control circuit (where trip coils are potential type)	Replace blown fuse
Faulty connections (loose or broken wire) in trip circuit	Repair faulty wiring, tighten all binding screws to proper torque value
OIL CONTAMINATED	
Carbonization from too many operations	Drain oil and filter, clean or replace. Add fresh oil. Clean inside of tank and all internal parts of breaker; refer to manufacturer's instructions
Condensation due to atmospheric conditions	Same procedure as above
Overheating	Eliminate cause of overheating

5-7. Instrumentation.

Switchgear instrumentation, based on the complexity of the complete system, may include all or any combination of indicating, recording, and metering instruments. Potential and current transformers are used to isolate instrument circuits from the power circuit. Usually, the secondary winding of potential transformers is rated at 120 volts. Current transformer output is 5 amperes.

a. *Types of instrumentation.* Instrumentation includes indicating and recording types.

b. *Application.* Information related to instrument transformer application is covered in paragraphs 5-3b(2) and 5-3c(2).

(1) *Voltage.* Voltage values are indicated by a voltmeter.

(2) *Current.* Current values are indicated by an ammeter.

(3) *Power.* Power values are described as watts, vars and power factor (refer to para 4-7e for additional information).

(a) *Watts.* Watts or kilowatts (units of electric power) are indicated by a wattmeter.

(b) *Vars.* Vars or kilovars (units of reactive power) are obtained by multiplying effective value of current, effective value of voltage and the sine of the angular phase difference between current and voltage.

(c) *Power factor.* Power factor, the ratio of active power to apparent power, is displayed on a power factor meter. The meter scale is usually graduated in percentage power factor.

(4) *Frequency.* Frequency of alternating current is indicated on a frequency meter. The meter scale is usually graduated in 50/60 Hertz.

(5) *Speed.* Rotational speed of the prime mover is indicated by a tachometer in revolutions per minute (rpm). Generating systems covered herein usually use an impulse tachometer, including the inductor and eddy current types. These tachometers use a magnetic pick-up to sense speed.

(6) *Temperature.* Several temperature values (including coolant, lubricating oil and exhaust) are usually required to assure safe prime mover operation. Each value is monitored by a sensing device with a remote indicator or thermometer. The sensing device can be thermocouple or a combination of sensing bulb and capillary tube.

(a) *Thermocouple.* A thermocouple consists of a pair of electrical conductors, each of different metal, which are joined at the end adjacent to the temperature to be measured. A thermal emf is produced at the junction of the conductors. The other end of each conductor is connected to a voltmeter which measures and indicates the thermal emf.

(b) *Sensing bulb and capillary tube.* The sensing bulb and capillary tube contain a specific amount of liquid or gas whose pressure varies with temperature. The variation appears on the thermometer and represents the temperature of coolant, oil or exhaust.

(7) *Pressure.* Pressure in the prime mover is indicated by sensing devices and remote gauges. Usually a bourdon tube is used. The variation appears on the gauge and represents lubricating oil or other pressure. Other pressure values may be shown on the system instrument panel depending on the type of prime mover and the overall system requirements. These pressure values include starting air, turbo boost, scavenging air, exhaust manifold and fuel gas. Gauges or meters are used for indication as required.

(8) *Fuel level.* Various methods are used for fuel level measurement. Fuel in underground storage tanks can be measured by immersing a calibrated dip stick in the tank. For day tanks, a glass sight-gauge or a float actuated gauge can be used to measure the quantity of liquid fuel, Remote indicators using pneumatic, electric or hydraulic devices are also used.

(9) *Running time.* The amount of time an auxiliary generating system operates is a required part of system record keeping. Time is usually recorded on a digital measuring device or counter located on the system instrument panel. Usually the counter is used with electric or electronic circuitry. An electric system usually has an AC synchronous motor that is geared to the counter. Accuracy of motor and

counter depends on the frequency of the generator output voltage. An electronic system also records operating time on a digital measuring device. This system measures time by counting the number of cycles produced by the frequency of the generator output voltage. Counter indications are proportional to frequency vs time.

5-8. Relays.

Relays are used with the automatic controls for auxiliary power generating systems. A relay responds to electrical or other operating parameters and causes an abrupt change in the control circuits when the measured values change. A relay consists of a sensing element and a control element with contacts.

a. Types of relays. Relays used in switchgear include general purpose and protective types.

(1) *General purpose.* General purpose relays function as part of regulation and verification devices throughout the system including the prime mover.

(a) Industrial. Portions of electrical systems are energized or de-energized under normal or abnormal conditions by relays. Since the relays are usually used with subsystems or equipment circuit breakers, the overall operating plan must be electrically coordinated. Coordination is usually accomplished by designing the system circuitry to selectively initiate the opening or closing of the relays. Relays constantly monitor the power system.

(b) Overload. 0verload relays are used to provide overload protection for the auxiliary motors. When an overload condition occurs in any of the three phases in which heaters are inserted, it will cause the relay to trip.

(c) Time delay. Relays employed for time delay purpose are usually solid-state type. Some pneumatic relays may still be in use. Pneumatic relays utilize a bellows type arrangement to provide the time delay. They can be adjusted for time periods of less than a second to several minutes.

(d) Solid-state. Solid-state relays derive their time delay from a combination of several electronic components. They are also adjustable between fractions of a second to several minutes.

(e) Voltage sensitive. Voltage sensitive relays are used to sense an increase or decrease in a specific voltage. They provide an output signal when the voltages pass the preset level.

(2) *Protective relays.* Protective relays detect, isolate, and/or indicate abnormal electrical conditions. The operation of circuit breakers or other protective devices is initiated by relays as required. Some of the electrical hazards protected against are short circuit, overcurrent, over or under voltage, and phase or frequency irregularities. Relays in-

stalled to protect generator stator windings from internal shorts and overheating are sensitive to faults in the generator and do not respond to faults outside the generator. These relays act rapidly to prevent damage to the generator and isolate the generator from the system. Relay action includes de-energizing the generator field winding. Protective relays are provided in systems when reverse power flow occurs. Those relays operate on a succession of power reversals and current impulses to detect loss of synchronism. Protective relays include the following types:

(a) Overcurrent. Overcurrent relays function when current flow exceeds the normal or desired value. Induction disk relays with time delay and cup type relays (without time delay) are known as electromechanical type relays. Solid state relays are normally used on more recently installed equipment.

(b) Overvoltage. Overvoltage relays function when voltage exceeds the normal or desired value. Induction disk relays with time delay and cup type relays without time delay are used.

(c) Undervoltage. Undervoltage relays function when voltage is less than normal or desired value. Induction disk relays with time delay may be used in a balanced position between minimum and maximum voltages.

(d) Reverse power. Reverse power relays function whenever power flows in the reverse direction from normal or desired. These relays detect loss of synchronism.

(e) Underfrequency. Underfrequency relays function whenever the desired frequency becomes less than normal value. This condition is usually the result of reduced prime mover speed and may be caused by the prime mover governor or excess electrical load.

(f) Differential. Differential relays function due to the difference between two quantities of the same kind such as, two currents or two voltages. Differential relays, usually used to detect stator winding electrical failure, respond to current percentage differences. Current or voltage transformers used in differential network should be in matched sets. Percentage differential relays are also used to prevent relay operation for faults due to current transformer ratio error outside the protected zone. In this application, the overcurrent relay operates instantly when there is a bus short circuit but will not operate if a current transformer secondary opens. The contacts of the two relays are connected in series.

(g) Current balance. A current balance relay circuit monitors two or more current circuits and provides an output if the difference between any

two exceeds the setting of the relay. The relay senses the difference between the current of one generator and the current of another generator or the average of all other generators. Relay output may be used to trip bus tie contactors and split a parallel system to remove an unbalance.

(h) Ground fault protection. Ground fault protection is usually provided by a ground sensor relay which measures the sum of currents in the lines to the load in a three-phase system. Another relay is sometimes added to the transformer neutral-to-ground connection for backup.

b. Testing of relays. Periodic testing of relays is considered preventive maintenance. The preventive maintenance program is built around records and visual inspections and includes analysis of the records.

(1) The frequency of testing is dependent on the variables involved i.e., type of relay, environmental conditions, history, and experience. The ambient operating temperature must be recorded. Most relays have draw-out construction so that a relay can be separated from its enclosure. Disconnection for test or repair is usually not required.

(2) Checks and tests to be performed are determined by the type of relay. The schedule for performance of tests should comply with the requirements of AR 420-43. Proceed as follows:

(a) Inspect the relay cover before testing. Remove dust and other foreign matter to prevent it from entering the relay. Record the inspection results.

(b) Check relay for "flag" indication. Also, check cover glass for fogging. If fogging is excessive, investigate the cause.

(c) Check all connections for proper tightness. If necessary, tighten to proper torque value.

(d) Check armature and connect gaps. Compare with previous measurements. Adjust gaps if necessary and refer to manufacturer's instructions.

(e) Check contacts for burned or eroded condition. Burnish if necessary and refer to manufacturer's instructions.

(f) Verify proper contact operation. Open or close contacts to observe proper trip or reclose action and refer to manufacturer's instructions.

(g) Apply current or voltage to verify that pickup is within manufacturer's tolerances.

(h) Reduce the current until the relay drops out or fully resets. Verify that there is no binding during operation and refer to manufacturer's instructions.

(i) Verify that related devices such as capacitors are functioning properly and refer to manufacturer's instructions.

(j) Note that differential relays are usually very sensitive devices that use polarized sensing circuitry. Repeat the pickup test. Use the second test for comparison with previous and future test data. Refer to manufacturer's instructions.

c. Record keeping. Equipment and system log sheets are important and necessary functions of record keeping. The log sheets must be specifically developed to suit auxiliary use.

d. Troubleshooting. Perform troubleshooting procedures when abnormal operation of the system or equipment is observed. Maintenance personnel must then refer to records for interpretation and comparison of performance data, i.e., log sheets. Comparisons of operation should be made under equal or closely similar conditions of load and ambient temperature. The general scheme for troubleshooting is outlined in the following table.

Table 5-3. Relay troubleshooting.

Note

Refer to manufacturer's literature for specific information on individual equipment.

Cause	Remedy
MAGNET-OPERATED INSTANTANEOUS TYPE	
High Trip Action	
Faulty coil	Install coil with correct rating
Low Trip Action	
Shorted turns on high trip	Test coil and replace with new coil if found defective
Mechanical binding; dirt, corrosion	Clean parts
Assembled incorrectly	See manufacturer's instructions
MAGNET-OPERATED INVERSE-TIME TYPE	
Slow Action Trip	
Fluid too heavy, vent too small, or temperature too low	Change fluid and open vent slightly, regulate temperature
Worn parts	Replace and adjust
Fast Trip Action	
Worn, broken parts	Replace and adjust
Fluid too light, vent too large or temperature too high	Change fluid to proper grade Close vent slightly or regulate temperature. Clean dashpots and refill with fresh fluid or proper grade
THERMAL TYPE	
Fails to Trip Causing Motor Burnout	
Wrong size heater	Check rating with recommendations on instruction sheet
Mechanical binding; dirt, corrosion	Clean and adjust
Relay damaged by short circuit	Replace relay
Motor and relay in different ambient temperature	install motor and control near each other or make temperature uniform for both

Table 5-3. Relay troubleshooting-Continued

Note

Refer to manufacturer's literature for specific information on individual equipment.

Cause	Remedy
Trips at Too Low Temperature	
Wrong heater	Check rating with manufacturer's instruction sheet
Assembled wrong	See manufacturer's instructions
Relay in high ambient temperature	Install controls closer to each other or make temperature uniform
Fails to Reset	
Broken mechanism; worn parts; corrosion, dirt	Replace broken parts, clean and adjust. Install new relay

5-9. Miscellaneous devices.

Miscellaneous devices include control switches, push buttons, indicating lights, batteries, surge capacitors, lightning arresters, maintenance tools, test equipment, and fuses.

a. Control switches and push buttons. Switchgear and related control panels contain complete controls for all functions of the auxiliary generator equipment. Control for voltage regulation, phase adjustment, current compensation, engine operating parameters as well as engine start, stop, and running speed, battery charging and brightness or dimming of indicator lights are usually provided.

b. Indicating lights. White indicating lamps with colored caps are used to show breaker positions. Green lights indicate open breakers, red lights indicated closed breakers. White lights, when used, are energized from potential transformers to indicate live circuits. Some stations include amber or orange lights to indicate that the circuit has been tripped automatically. Low voltage lamps, connected in series with appropriate resistors, are usually used to reduce lamp size and glare. Red and green lights are usually wired so that they are energized through the trip coil of the breaker. An opening in the trip coil circuit is indicated by a dark unlit lamp. Similar indicating lamps and colored caps are used to indicate normal and abnormal conditions for other control functions of the system.

c. Batteries. Storage batteries and battery systems are frequently a part of an auxiliary power system. Batteries are used for prime mover cranking, or an uninterruptible power system. The batteries maintain a charge through the application of a "floating" battery charger. As the battery discharges its energy the charger increases its charge rate by increasing the flow of current into the battery. The converse is true as the battery reaches a full charge, a very small current flows into the battery. In addition, batteries provide power for switchgear control and power to trip some circuit breakers. Most applications for auxiliary power use some form of "wet" lead acid battery, however, some systems use "dry" nickel cadmium (nicad) batteries. Both types of batteries produce direct current repeatedly by chemical reactions. Batteries must be recharged after each use to restore their power. Wet cell batteries require scheduled maintenance. This includes a visual inspection of all cells, a weekly hydrometer reading of the sample cell, and monthly readings of floating voltage, water level, hydrometer, and temperature of each cell. Cell connectors must be kept clean and tight to prevent heating due to high resistance or voltage drop. Tops of cells must be kept free of dirt or conductive materials. Charging area must be exhausted to positively prevent hydrogen build up and explosion.

d. Surge capacitors. Surge absorbing capacitors are sometime used, with or without lightning arresters, to modify the shape of the surge voltage wave. These capacitors operate at voltages of 240, 480, 600 and higher for single or three-phase operation. Capacitor banks, formed by individual units connected in parallel, are sometimes used. Fuses and circuit breakers with time-current characteristics are used to prevent rupture of the capacitor case under severe conditions. Safety precautions must be observed when working on capacitors.

(1) Surge capacitors using polychlorinated biphenyls (PCBs) may still be in use. Refer to 40 CFR 761. Since PCBs are carcinogenic and are not biodegradable, some restrictions to their use apply.

(2) Special handling is required if PCBs are used in any equipment. PCBs are powerful solvents. Handling and disposal information and special gloves are available in the base engineer's office.

e. Lightning arresters. A lightning arrester (a protective device) limits voltage caused by a lightning strike and bypasses the related current surge to a ground system which absorbs most of the strike energy. An overvoltage condition can also be caused by a fault in the electrical system.

(1) There are two general types of arrester designs, valve type and expulsion type. The valve type has one or more sets of spark gaps (series connected) which establish spark-over voltage, interrupt the flow of current, and prevent high current flow. The expulsion type has an arc extinguishing chamber in series with the gaps to interrupt the power frequency current which flows after the gaps have been sparked over. Design refinements include using oxide film coated components and sealing the inner components in a chamber filled with an inert gas. Aluminum cells are used in some units.

(2) Installed lightning arresters can retain a lethal electric charge. Accordingly, lightning arresters must be considered as loaded to full circuit potential unless disconnected from the circuit and grounded.

f. Special maintenance tools. Always use the proper tool for the job being done. Avoid the use of improvised tools or tools in poor condition. Store tools not in use properly.

(1) Hand tools include the following: screwdrivers, pliers, wrenches, wire insulation strippers, and wire cutters.

(2) Powered hand tools include the following: hydraulic, pneumatic and electrical. Unless an electrical tool is battery powered or double insulated, make sure the tool has a line cord with a grounded conductor and polarized grounding plug. Make sure the receptacle to be used is properly grounded.

(3) Machine tools include grinding wheels and cutting tools.

g. Test equipment. Before using any test equipment make sure that it has valid calibration certification. Test equipment required for switchgear maintenance usually includes many or all of the following items.

(1) *Multimeter.* The multimeter is sometimes called a volt-ohm-milliammeter or VOM. It is a single test instrument with a number of different ranges for measuring voltage, current, and resistance.

(2) *Voltmeter.* An instrument used for measuring voltage. Its scale indicates microvolts, millivolts, volts or kilovolts.

(3) *Voltammeter.* An instrument used as either a voltmeter or an ammeter.

(4) *Ohmmeter.* An instrument used for measuring resistance. It consists of a DC milliammeter, a DC source, and a resistor network.

(5) *Ammeter.* An instrument that measures the amount of current in amperes. Its meter shows current value in microamperes, milliamperes, or kiloamperes.

(6) *Frequency meter.* An instrument for measuring the frequency of an alternating current. Its scale shows Hertz (cycles per second), kiloHertz (kilocycles), or megaHertz (megacycles).

(7) *Wattmeter.* An instrument for measuring electric power. Its scale is usually graduated in watts or kilowatts.

(8) *Megohmmeter.* A device that is a high range ohmmeter, sometimes referred to as a megger. It consists of a hand driven, motor driven, or battery driven generator as the DC source, and a meter. It is used to measure insulation resistance and other high resistance. It can be used to check for continuity, grounds, and short circuits.

(9) *Electrical analyzer:* An instrument for measuring the various parameters of AC circuits. It consists of a voltmeter, ammeter, wattmeter, and power factor meter. The analyzer also includes two current transformers and switches necessary for use. It can be used for testing insulation.

(10) *Certification.* Test equipment should have valid calibration certification.

h. Fuses. Fuses detect circuit overload conditions and open when there is too much current flowing. Fuses are the safety valves of the installation's electrical system and provide the most economical type of circuit protection.

(1) *Application.* There are many types of fuses with various characteristics. Always verify that a fuse, whether a new or replacement unit, is of the proper type and rating before installing. Never arbitrarily replace one type of fuse with another fuse of the same physical size just because it fits the fuse holder. The fuse used should have the correct current and voltage ratings, proper time delay and current limiting characteristics and an adequate interrupting rating to protect the circuit and its components. Fuse holders should never be altered or forced to accept fuses which do not fit.

(2) *Construction.* A fuse consists of two main parts: the fusible link and the enclosing housing or body. The link is a metallic alloy that melts when excessive current flows through it, thereby breaking the circuit. When the current heats the alloy to its melting point, the link breaks and an arc forms. Melting continues rapidly until the resultant gap is too wide for the arc to span. A fuse usually can carry a 100 percent load indefinitely and will blow in a specified time at 150 percent overload. The following fuse types are usually used.

(a) *Current limiting fuses.* Current limiting fuses are used where necessary to limit the amount of fault energy flowing through a fuse to the circuit. A fuse must clear a fault in less than ½ cycle of the fault current sine wave to be considered a current limiting fuse. If the fault current is allowed to flow for ½ cycle or more, the maximum (peak) fault current is passed through the fuse. A current limiting fuse must act quickly to limit the energy let through the fuse to the protected circuit. The total clearing time of a fuse is made up of two components; the melting time, and the arcing time. The fault current reaches maximum at the conclusion of the melting time, much less than ¼ cycle. An arc is established inside the fuse at the conclusion of the melting time. The arc presents a high resistance to the flow of fault current and the current decays to zero, clearing the fault. Whenever possible de-energize the fuse-holder circuit before removing or installing a fuse.

(b) *Metal-enclosed fuse.* Fuse enclosed in an oil filled metal housing and used (up to 7,500 volts) for protecting transformer banks and other distribution elements. Refer to the manufacturer's literature for details.

(c) *Glass-enclosed fuse.* Fuse enclosed in a glass tube filled with arc quenching liquid. Carbon tetrachloride is the liquid frequently used. Refer to the manufacturer's literature for details.

(d) *Expilsion fuse.* Fuse enclosed in a fiber tube filled with dry (powdered) boric acid. When the fuse element blows, the boric acid produces a gas which aids in promptly deionizing the arc. Used on circuits up to 138 kV. Refer to the manufacturer's literature for details.

(3) Checks *and examinations.* Examine fuse terminals and holders for discoloration caused by heat from poor contact and/or corrosion. Checks to be performed are determined by the type of fuse and fuse holder, proceed as follows:

(a) Inspect fuse and fuse holder contact surfaces for pitting, burning, alignment, and spring pressure. Badly pitted or burned components must be replaced.

(b) Examine the fuse unit, and renewable element if the fuse type is used, for corrosion. Check for signs of discharge tracking on the fuse. Replace components that show deterioration.

(c) Verify that all attaching parts are installed and tightened to proper torque value.

(d) Check fuse tubes made of fiber or other organic material. Refinish the fuse tube as required. Refer to manufacturer's literature.

(e) Check vented expulsion fuses. Some fuses may have condensers or mufflers to restrict expulsion of gases during operation. A dropout feature that automatically disengages the fuse when it operates may be used. These fuses usually have seals to keep moisture out of the interrupting chamber. Refer to manufacturer's literature for instructions.

(f) Replace fuse holders and clips which are worn or make poor contact. Remove oxidation and corrosion from fuses, holders and clips. Determine the causes of overheating and correct as required.

i. *Synchroscope.* A synchroscope, usually installed on a switchgear control panel, is used to determine the phase difference or degree of synchronism of two alternating current quantities or two generators. The synchronism always indicates the condition of the incoming machine with respect to the bus. If the frequency of the incoming machine is higher than the bus frequency, the synchroscope point revolves in the "fast" direction. If the frequency of the incoming machine is lower than the bus frequency, the synchroscope pointer revolves in the "slow" direction. If the pointer stops at a position other than 0 degrees, it indicates that the incoming machine is at the same frequency as the bus but out of phase. Correct the phase error by adjusting the prime mover governor of the incoming machine for higher speed. The synchroscope pointer should revolve slowly in the "fast" direction. The machines are paralleled when the pointer reaches the 0 degree position while traveling in the "fast" direction. When paralleled, the pointer will stay at 0 degrees. Refer to manufacturer's literature for specific operation and inspection information on individual equipment.

CHAPTER 6
OPERATING PROCEDURES

6-1. Requirements.

A successfully operating auxiliary power generating system has several requirements. First, the equipment in the system must be selected with ease of operation and maintenance as prime considerations. Second, the equipment must be installed by competent personnel.

a. Adequate records must be kept during installation and operational shakedown so that any future modifications can be implemented with minimal research. Third, the operating personnel must be thoroughly trained in proper operating procedures. Training must include performance of maintenance as well as operation. Fourth, a detailed record keeping system must be instituted.

b. The record keeping system must include a library of the various equipment manufacturers' instructions, operating log sheets, routine maintenance instructions, maintenance log sheets, and piping and electrical drawings. The records should be assembled in binders or folders and stored in the installation's engineering office for availability and safekeeping.

6-2. Attended stations.

a. Attended stations have one or more operators on duty around the clock or for a portion of the day if the plant is not used full time. Plants that have an operator on duty only for a portion of the day sometimes require an operator's presence during the entire period that the plant is supplying power to the system. Attended stations can be operated in a manual mode, a semi-automatic mode, or an automatic mode. If the plant is manned at all times, the manual or semi-automatic mode is usually employed. In the manual mode, the operator has complete control of the power plant and would start the prime mover, bring it to operating speed, apply excitation to the generator, and close the circuit breaker to pick up the station load. When paralleling with another generator, the operator must perform the paralleling procedures described in paragraph 6-6. If paralleling with the electric utility system is desired, approval must be obtained from the utility and the need for special relaying, such as reverse power relays, must be determined. The procedures for parallel utility operation are described in paragraph 6-5.

b. In the semi-automatic mode, sensing devices monitor the normal source of power. Upon a loss of the normal power source, the sensing devices are activated and initiate a starting signal to the prime mover. An alarm circuit is also initiated at this time to alert the operator that normal power has been lost and the emergency unit has started. As the prime mover approaches rated speed, excitation is automatically applied to the generator. The power plant will then remain in this condition, i.e., rated speed and voltage, until the operator closes the circuit breaker connecting the emergency generator to the load. If the station has more than one generator, and the load requires more than one generator, the operator must initiate the synchronizing circuitry. Using the techniques provided in paragraphs 6-5 and 6-6, the operator must parallel the second generator with the first. If additional generators are required, they must be added to the system in the same manner. The operator can then adjust the governors and excitation controls to obtain the desired load division and reactive power division between generators.

c. The automatic mode is similar to the semi-automatic mode up to the point that the unit reaches rated speed and voltage. When the speed and voltage have stabilized, if the unit is picking up a completely dead plant, a closing signal is initiated to the circuit breaker. The circuit breaker energizes the desired loads. If the load demands more than one unit, as the second unit reaches its operating speed and voltage, automatic synchronizing circuitry is enabled. The speed of the incoming unit will be adjusted automatically, and when the synchronizing relay is satisfied that the conditions are correct, a closing signal to the circuit breaker for the second unit will be sent. If additional units are needed, the automatic synchronizing circuitry will be switched as the units become available. Once normal power is again available, the procedure for returning the load to the normal bus is usually done in the manual mode. Installations that permit paralleling with the electric utility system can retransfer without an interruption of power. If paralleling is not permitted, there will be a momentary outage when the switching is performed. Some installations are designed with an automatic retransfer to normal power. However, these are usually the smaller-rated units that use a transfer switch arrangement rather than circuit breakers for switching loads.

6-3. Unattended stations.

Unattended stations operate without an operator in attendance. Their operation is the same as an attended station used in the automatic mode.

6-4. Nonparalleled stations.

a. Nonparalleled stations are those stations that do not have provisions for connecting the emergency generator bus to the commercial bus. It also applies to a station that has a tie breaker between two incoming lines that, because of electric utility regulations, cannot be connected together. Electrical interlocks are used to prevent an unwanted paralleling from occurring. These interlocks usually consist of two circuit breakers electrically connected. The arrangement is such that only one circuit breaker can be in the closed position at a time, thus preventing paralleling.

b. In some arrangements, mechanical interlocks may also be provided. A mechanical interlock is a device that physically prevents both circuit breakers from being closed at the same time. This method also prevents paralleling from occurring.

c. Immediately before starting the prime movers, make a thorough inspection to insure that the following is in order. Verify that engine generator is not set to operate in a semi-automatic or automatic starting mode during prime mover inspections. If not, extreme caution should be used. Unexpected start of prime mover while inspecting can lead to severe injury or death. Check for leaks in the lubricating system, the fuel system, and the cooling system. If any of the auxiliaries are belt-driven, check for tightness of the belts. Check for proper levels of oil, water and fuel. Look for tools or other loose objects, such as rags, that may have been left in the area, and remove. If air pressure is a part of the starting system, make sure the air pressure is at the correct value. Verify that none of the intake air vents or exhaust ports are blocked. Start auxiliary pumps (lube oil, fuel or water) that are necessary prior to running the unit.

d. When the preparations for starting have been completed, a start signal is given to the prime mover. The engine (prime mover) should start to rotate and, under control of the governor, accelerate to idling speed. Once the speed has stabilized, read the pressure and temperature gauges to make sure that normal pressure and temperatures are being maintained. Listen to any unusual noises. Shut the engine down if any unusual pressures or temperatures are observed, or if unusual noises are heard. Be familiar with the engine manufacturer's literature for information on acceptable pressures and temperatures. Once the unit has been placed under load, readings should be taken according to the operating log developed for that station. When the unit is no longer required and the load has been removed, operate the engine at no load, or at some preset idle speed to allow the engine to cool gradually. When the cooling period has expired, shut the engine down. Cooling periods vary for different prime movers. Refer to manufacturer's instructions. Stop the auxiliaries that do not stop automatically. Make an inspection of the unit, looking for any unusual conditions.

e. It is essential that each power generator have a complete set of standard operating procedures. The procedures include an up-to-date one-line diagram of the electrical system showing the generators and the associated switchgear components (see fig 6-l). Notes and legends are usually included with the diagram.

AM Ammeter	AS Ammeter Switch
VA4 Voltmeter	VS Voltmeter Switch
WM Wutt-hour Meter	WHDM Wutt-hour Demand Meter
CPT Control Power Transformer	VAR Volt-Ampere Meter
CT Current Transformer	PT Potential Transformer
G1,G2 Generators	FU Fuse

f. Before the unit is started an inspection should be made. This can be done in conjunction with the inspection of the prime mover. Look for any material or loose parts that could be drawn into the generator. Make sure that the air flow will not be restricted either on the intake or exhaust.

g. When the prime mover has the generator at operating speed, excitation can be applied. Adjust the voltage regulator until the generator is at rated voltage. Adjust the governor control for the prime mover so that the generator is at rated frequency. Close the main circuit breaker connecting the generator to the load. If necessary adjust the voltage control for rated voltage and the governor control for rated frequency. Readings of various parameters are taken according to the operating log for that station. Care must be taken so that the generator is operated at or below its nameplate rating. After the unit has been shut down, a visual inspection similar to that performed prior to startup can be performed.

h. Proper operation of the switchgear requires a knowledge of the standard operating procedures and the familiarity with the one-line diagram of the electrical system. It requires some knowledge of the various protective relays and other devices associated with the system. The operator must be able to recognize an impending problem by observing the meters or other indicators. The operator can then take proper action. The operator must be able to perform some basic troubleshooting and maintenance.

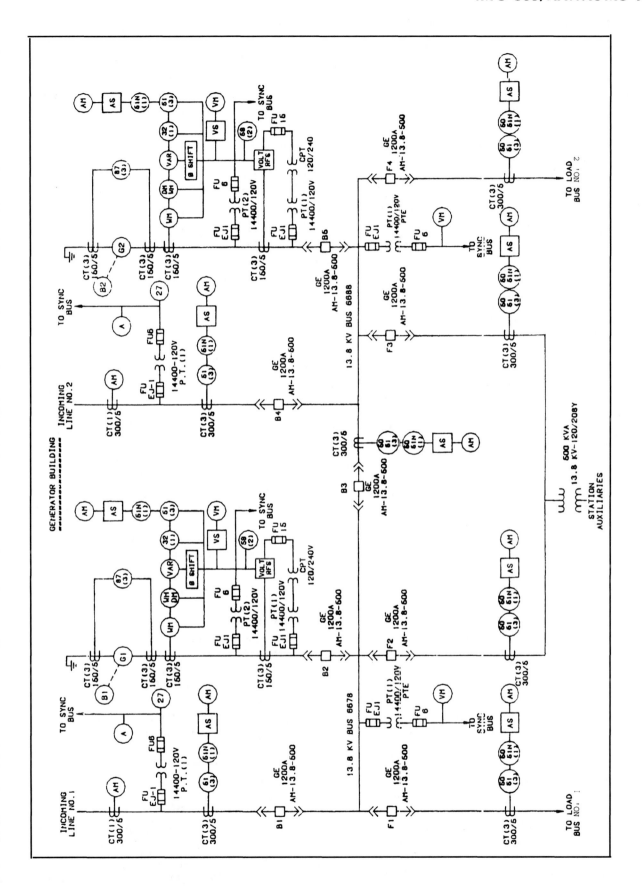

Figure 6–1. Typical station layout, one-line diagram.

6-5. Paralleled with the electric utility system.

a. Stations that can be paralleled with electric utility systems have the same basic characteristics as those discussed in paragraph 6-2. They have additional features including synchronizing circuitry and, in the case of the unattended station, an automatic mode.

b. The prime movers in these stations can be operated in the manual or automatic mode. Operation in the manual mode is discussed in paragraph 6-2a. In the automatic mode, relays in the switchgear will sense the loss of commercial power and provide a starting signal to the prime mover. It will then accelerate under control of the governor to the operating speed. The remainder of the prime mover operation is as previously discussed.

c. This discussion is the same as paragraph 6-4d with the exception that if the station is in automatic, excitation will be applied by the automatic circuitry. Also, in automatic the main circuit breaker will close automatically, provided the incoming line circuit breaker is open.

d. The comments regarding proper switchgear operation as noted in paragraph 6-4h pertain to paralleling with the utility system. In addition, this type of system requires paralleling circuitry which is part of the switchgear. It includes one or more synchronizing switches, a synchroscope, synchronizing lights, incoming voltmeter, incoming frequency meter, running voltmeter, and a running frequency meter. The synchronizing circuitry is energized by turning the synchronizing switch on.

e. The synchroscope indicates the condition of the incoming machine with respect to the bus. If the frequency of the incoming machine is higher than that of the bus, the synchroscope pointer will revolve in a clockwise or "fast" direction. The operator should adjust the governor control of the incoming prime mover until the synchroscope pointer is revolving slowly in the "fast" direction. The machines should be paralleled by closing the breaker of the incoming generator when the pointer reaches 12 o'clock. Because there is a slight lag in the breaker or switching mechanism, it is good practice to start the breaker closing operation at about the 11:30 position or slightly before the pointer reaches 12 o'clock.

f. Synchronizing lamps provide a means of checking the synchroscope for proper operation. As the pointer revolves, the lamps go alternately bright and dark in unison. Both lamps must be dark as the pointer passes 12 o'clock or the synchroscope is defective.

g. Now that the generator is paralleled with the electric utility system, the load (kW) can be controlled by adjusting the governor control. The reactive load (vars) can be controlled by adjusting the voltage control. To remove load from the generator, reduce the load by decreasing the governor control while observing the kW meter for the generator. When the kW meter indicates zero, open the generator circuit breaker. The load will now be transferred to the electric utility bus. The prime mover can then be shut down by following normal procedures.

6-6. Paralleled with other generating units.

a. Stations that have two or more generators that can be operated in parallel have the same basic characteristics as previously discussed in paragraphs 6-2 and 6-3. In addition, they may have automatic synchronizing circuitry and also droop circuits for the voltage regulators. The automatic synchronizing circuitry includes speed-matching relays, voltage-matching relays, and automatic synchronizing relays. These relays function when the station is in the automatic mode and when two or more AC sources are in agreement within specified limits of phase angle and frequency. The voltage regulator droop circuits are energized when two or more generators are operated in parallel. Their purpose is to prevent the undesirable condition of circulating currents between generators.

b. Parallel operation of generators with regulators is accomplished by appropriate cross-current compensation. The method employs an equalizing reactor or compensator which adds a small voltage, proportional to the reactive current delivered by the generator, to the voltage delivered by the potential transformers. This gives a slight droop to the voltage held by the regulator on reactive loads and divides reactive currents in proportion to load currents. Differential compensation is used when line-droop compensators are installed to automatically increase the voltage as the load increases. With this connection, all the equalizing reactors or compensators are connected in series. There is no current flow in the equalizing reactors under balanced load conditions. If the load is unbalanced, the currents flow through the regulators to decrease the excitation of the generator carrying excessive reactive currents. This increases the excitation of the generator carrying low reactive current.

6-7. Operational testing.

a. Emergency generator power units must be operated under load conditions periodically to insure their reliability. The period for this exercising will vary from station to station. It is important that accurate logs be kept of the conditions encountered during the exercising.

b. It is suggested that the manufacturer of the auxiliary power unit be consulted to determine the time intervals in which the auxiliary power unit should be exercised and the length of each exercise. National and local codes may enter into this consideration.

c. The procedures used for exercising the units will also vary from station to station. The most desirable condition is to use the actual load. However, this is not always possible and in these cases a load bank can be used. A load bank is generally a portable set of resistors that allows a generator to be tested under load by disconnecting the generator from the actual load and connecting it to the load bank. In those stations that permit paralleling with the electric utility system another method is used. After paralleling, the load on the generator can be controlled by adjusting the governor control.

d. In addition to exercising the units, it is also desirable to periodically perform an operational test. This test is accomplished by opening the circuit breaker from the electric utility and verifying that the necessary relays and contactors energize such that the emergency generator breaker closes and starts the auxiliary power generating system. Performance of the test simulates a loss of commercial power. The frequency of this test is dependent on the nature of the load, i.e., critical or non critical, but is usually performed on a monthly basis.

CHAPTER 7

ROUTINE MAINTENANCE

7-1. Instructions.

a. Manufacturers provide specific instructions for the use and care of each of their products. Their instructions are the result of wide experience obtained under varying conditions and should be followed closely. Maintenance personnel should always check equipment first for signs of physical damage before performing any other checks.

b. Routine maintenance instructions consist of scheduled inspections of prime movers, generators and exciters, and switchgear. When a need for service or repair is indicated, refer to the manufacturer's literature for specific information. Service records of the auxiliary power systems are filed in the installation's engineering office.

c. Maintenance information provided in this manual supplements the manufacturer's instructions but does not supersede them. Checklists and schedules furnished herein are intended as guides for operators and service personnel.

d. Since auxiliary power systems are operated intermittently, the usual time frames for routine maintenance such as weekly, monthly, quarterly, annually may not apply. Accordingly, "short-term" is used for tasks to be performed less frequently. Exceptions are noted in the manufacturer's manual.

e. Electrical systems acceptance tests are functional tests to verify the proper interaction on all sensing, processing, and action electrical devices. It is critical that these tests be performed on standby generator power systems to ascertain the safe and operational reliability of a system. A system must be tested as a united series of devices in addition to the testing of individual components. For systems that include auto-start, auto-transfer, and/or auto-synchronizing equipment, every six months utility electrical power should be removed (open main circuit breaker) from a building, or part of the facility that is supplied electrical power by commercial power/generation combination to ascertain that the system will operate under abnormal conditions.

7-2. Prime mover maintenance.

Routine maintenance instructions for prime movers consist of short- and long-term checklists for diesel and gas turbine engines.

a. Short-term (diesels). Short-term checklist for diesel engines.

(1) *General comments.* Before performing any tasks required by the following checklist, review the station log sheets, related records, and the manufacturer's recommendations.

(2) *Checklist.*

(a) *Values.* Check valve operation.

(b) *Fuel injection nozzles.* Check fuel injection nozzles for secure mounting and connections each time the engine is shut down. Torque down the nozzles according to the manufacturer's instructions.

(c) *Starting system.* Check the general condition of the air compressor, air lines, and valves, when applicable. Briefly pop open the system's safety valve weekly. Check for proper operation. Refer to manufacturer's instructions for details.

(d) *Governor alarms and instruments.* Check operation of governor alarms and instruments. Refer to manufacturer's instructions'

(e) *Pressure gauges.* Check pressure gauges and clean exposed indicating elements. Refer to manufacturer's instructions.

(f) *Intake and exhaust systems.* Check air filters and engine exhaust. A smoking exhaust indicates incorrect adjustments. Clean air filters as necessary.

(g) *Exhaust Lines.* Clean and inspect exhaust lines. On two-cycle engines, remove carbon from exhaust ports and clean thermocouples. Refer to manufacturer's instructions for frequency of checks.

(h) *Evaporative cooling.* Refer to manufacturer's instructions for cooling tower maintenance. Inspect and oil fanshaft bearings, oil damper bearings and linkage. Inspect spray nozzles; clean as necessary. Clean pump suction screen. Clean sump pan. Inspect cooling coil. If scale has formed, circulate cleaning solution. Do not operate fan while cleaning coil. Check belts for condition and proper tension. Refer to manufacturer's instructions.

(i) *Fuel oil system.* Clean fuel oil strainers as required by operating conditions. Check the system components for clean condition. Refer to manufacturer's recommendations.

(j) *Fuel filters and centrifuges.* Check fuel oil filters and centrifuges. Check fuel oil system for leaks and correct as required. Refer to manufacturer's instructions.

(k) *Lubricating systems.* Check mechanical lubrication hourly during operation. Oil all hand lubrication points, following manufacturer's instructions. Correct leaks.

(l) Sight-feed Lubricators. Clean sight-feed lubricating oil strainers as necessary. Check for adequate lubricant supply.

(m) Lubricating oil filters. Check lubricating oil filters. Clean and replace filter elements as necessary.

(n) Piston assembly and connecting rods. On two-cycle engines, remove upper handhole inspection cover from side of engine immediately after the engine is shut down, and inspect the piston for proper lubrication.

(o) Cylinders and cylinder heads. Use compressed air to blow out indicator connections. Clean indicators and install. Refer to manufacturer's instructions.

(p) Crankshaft, crankpin and main bearings. Remove crankcase covers immediately after engine is shut down. Check main and crankpin bearings for proper lubrication. Check bearing temperatures for excessive heat by hand-touch. Refer to manufacturer's instructions for frequency of checks.

(q) Gauges and instruments. Verify that gauges and instruments have up-to-date calibration certifications. Read and record all indications of gauges, thermometers and other instruments at regular intervals as required by the operating log.

(r) Turbocharger. Observe every four hours during operation. Check for general condition and signs of vibration. Evaluate vibration if present.

(s) Turbocharger impeller. Check turbocharger impeller for accumulated dirt and axial endplay. Dirt may indicate faulty filtering equipment. Clean and service according to manufacturer's instructions.

b. Long- term (diesels). Long-term checklist for diesel engines. Performance of checklist tasks is related to frequency and extent of use of the auxiliary power plant.

(1) General comments. The following tasks should be performed annually, unless otherwise noted, following performance of short-term checks.

(2) Checklist and schedule.

(a) Valve inspection. Inspect exhaust valves; clean and remove carbon on two-cycle engines and valves as necessary. Refer to manufacturer's instructions.

(b) Inlet valves. Inspect and regrind inlet and exhaust valves and valve seats as necessary. Refer to manufacturer's instructions.

(c) Valve springs and guides. Check valve spring length and tension and inspect valve stems, bushings, and guides annually or after 2000 hours of use, whichever comes first. Replace parts as necessary. Refer to manufacturer's instructions.

(d) Camshaft and drive. Check and adjust gears and/or timing chain. Refer to manufacturer's instructions.

(e) Camshaft bearings. Inspect and adjust camshaft bearing clearances. Refer to manufacturer's instructions.

(f) Fuel injection nozzle inspection. After 2000 hours of use, remove and check nozzles in the test stand. Service and adjust nozzles following manufacturer's instruction.

(g) Fuel injection pumps. Inspect fuel injection pumps for secure mounting, cleanliness, and proper operation.

(h) Fuel injection pump inspection. Disassemble and recondition all injection pump nozzles after 2000 hours of use. Repair or replace worn or damaged parts. Reassemble and adjust, following the manufacturer's instructions.

(i) Air Lines. Drain water from air lines and tank monthly or as necessary. Drain valves are usually located at the lowest point(s) in the air feed system.

(j) Air valves. Clean air valves and reseat if necessary. Refer to manufacturer's instructions.

(k) Air compressor. Disassemble and overhaul the air compressor and starting equipment every five years based on frequency of use of the auxiliary power plant.

(l) Pressure gauge inspection. Check the date of calibration. Verify that gauges have valid calibration certification. Calibrate per manufacturer's instructions as required.

(m) Governor overhaul. Overhaul the governor after 2000 hours of use or when needed as indicated. Repair or replace worn or damaged parts. Reassemble and adjust, following the manufacturer's instructions.

(n) Muffler (silencer). Keep the muffler and waste heat equipment, boiler or heat exchange clean. Accumulations of unburned lubricating oil and soot or carbon are potential fire hazards. Make sure fuel combustion is as efficient as possible. Refer to manufacturer's instructions.

(o) Cooling systems. Inspect piping and valves for leaks and clean the heat exchanger. Perform cooling system maintenance, refer to appendix D, herein, and manufacturer's instructions.

(p) Cooling tower. Drain and clean cooling tower; clean and inspect piping, circulating pumps and equipment. Refer to appendix D.

(q) Cooling system service. Clean and inspect entire cooling system yearly. Overhaul pumps and recondition valves and other equipment as necessary. Refer to manufacturer's instructions.

(r) Fuel oil tanks and lines. Drain service tanks and lines. Remove water and sediment. Check heating coil for proper operation. Refer to appendix B.

(s) Lubricating oil cooler. Clean and inspect lubricating oil cooler for leaks and good condition. Clean outer surfaces more often under dusty operating conditions for more efficient cooling. Refer to manufacturer's instructions.

(t) Crankcase. Drain crankcase semi- annually or more frequent based on number of hours run per manufacturer's recommendations or acceptable industrial engine maintenance procedures. Inspect lubricating oil pumps; flush crankcase and refill. Refer to manufacturer's instructions and to the Army Oil Analysis Program (TB 43-0210) for instructions.

(u) Lubricating oil pump. Inspect the pump after 2000 hours of use for proper operation. Refer to manufacturer's specifications for the pump.

(v) Cylinder heads. Remove cylinder heads according to the manufacturer's instructions after 2000 hours of use. Inspect cylinder liners. Clean and inspect water jackets. Remove scale&and corrosion as necessary. Inspect and measure diameter of cylinder liners. Check gaskets for annealing, brittleness or cracks. Install new gaskets if necessary.

(w) Piston assembly inspection. On four-cycle engines, pull one piston after 2000 hours of use and inspect for proper cooling, lubrication and carbon deposits. Inspect piston rings and wrist pin and the cylinder liner for compliance with engine manufacturer's specifications.

(x) Inspection of pistons. Pull pistons after 4000 hours of engine use. Clean and inspect all parts for wear, proper lubrication and cooling. Verify that rings and ring clearances comply with engine manufacturer's specifications.

(y) Cylinder inspection. Use the barring device (jacking bar) to turn each piston to top dead center during step x. Inspect each cylinder liner for scoring. Refer to manufacturer's instructions.

(z) Anchor bolts. Check anchor bolts for proper torque value.

(aa) Flywheel bolts. Check flywheel bolts for proper torque value. Refer to manufacturer's instructions. Verify alignment and coupling to generator, comply with specifications.

(ab) Main and crankpin bearings. Remove bearing caps; check journals and bearings for proper lubrication, wear or scoring. Check main bearings for proper alignment. Refer to manufacturer's instructions.

(ac) Crankshaft. Verify compliance with engine manufacturer's specifications. Examine crankshaft for cracks. Measure distance between crankwebs for crankshaft deflection. Check journal level and clean oil passages. Replace bearings as necessary and adjust running clearance following the manufacturer's instructions.

(ad) Turbocharger inspection. Disassemble, clean and inspect entire turbocharger following the manufacturer's instructions and specifications.

(ae) General overhaul. Overhaul diesel engines and driven equipment every ten years or about 16,000 hours of auxiliary use. Follow the manufacturer's recommendations and instructions. Comply with the manufacturer's specifications.

c. Short-term (gas turbines). Short-term checklist for gas turbines. Checks are limited to inspection and cleaning tasks that can be performed on the exterior of an engine.

(1) General Comments. Before performing any tasks required by the following checklist, review the station log sheets, related records and the manufacturer's recommendations.

(2) The following precautions must be met. Shut the engine down. Apply "Do not operate" tags to the operating controls. Open the engine automatic start circuit. Deactivate the fire extinguishing system. Keep all engine enclosure doors open while working on the engine. Allow engine to cool down before working on it.

(3) Checklist.

(a) Inlet inspection. Verify that the inlet drain at lower part of duct is open and free of any obstruction so that moisture (rain or condensation) can run off. Check inlet temperature sensor for signs of damage. Clean sensor and surrounding area with approved solvent to remove dirt and contaminants. Refer to manufacturer's instructions. Make sure sensor is securely attached to engine.

(b) Exhaust inspection. Visually inspect engine exhaust casing, struts, and center body for cracks, nicks and other signs of damage. Refer to manufacturer's instructions. Inspect exhaust stack for freedom from obstructions and general good condition.

(c) Chip detectors. Engines usually have plugs with magnetic chip detectors at lubrication sumps. During normal operation, some fuzz-like particles will be found on the detectors. Also, other materials (non-metallic sludge and/or flakes, bronze powder, aluminum chips, etc.) may accumulate on the plugs. Refer to manufacturer's literature for specific information. Check chip detectors for electrical continuity while installed. Continuity is an indication of contamination. Remove chip detectors if contaminated. Discard packing and clean chip detector. Check chip detector for good thread and proper magnetism. Place new packings on chip de-

tectors and install on engine. Tighten to proper torque.

(d) External inspection. Inspect engine tubes, hoses, tube/hose fittings, electrical assemblies and connectors for security, and overheating and damage due to leakage. Perform inlet and exhaust inspection as described previously. Check standoffs, brackets and struts for looseness, cracks, and damage. Check ignition exciter, igniter plugs and leads for damage, overheating and security. Check mechanical control for signs of excessive wear, damage and security. Check fuel manifold for leaks, signs of damage and security. Check for rust and/or corrosion.

d. Long-term (gas turbines). Long-term checks usually affect interior areas of the engine and are seldom performed in the field. Repairs, if necessary, may involve changes in component balance relationships and should be performed at the designated overhaul location. Refer to the manufacturer's literature for information.

7-3. Generators and exciters.

Routine maintenance instructions for generators and exciters consist of short- and long-term checklists for rotating and static type equipment.

a. Short-term. Short-term checklists for generators and exciters.

(1) General comments. Before performing any tasks required by the following checklist, review the station log sheets, related records and the manufacturer's recommendations.

(2) Checklist.

(a) Air screens or filters. Air screens or filters should be changed when the air flow is restricted enough to increase generator operating temperature. Refer to manufacturer's literature.

(b) Exciter coupling (if applicable). When the generator unit is shut down prior to operation, wipe off excess lubrication from the coupling to prevent spatter.

(c) Coupling Leaks and alignment. When the generator has been shut down, check for lubrication leaks and tightness of coupling. Note any evidence of improper alignment and correct if necessary.

(d) Axial position. Check axial position of the prime mover, generator and exciter shafts for correct alignment and angularity.

(e) Bearings. Lubrication of generator and exciter bearings is required. Refer to manufacturer's literature for instructions for pressure and nonpressure lubricated bearings.

(f) Rotary exciters. Brushes and brush rigging. Remove carbon dust from collector ring and commutator with vacuum and dry with compressed

air at about 25 psi monthly. Check brushes for wear and indications of arcing and chattering monthly. Check condition of slip rings. Refer to manufacturer's instructions.

(g) Static exciters. Verify that the equipment is clean and free from dirt and moisture. Verify that all connections are tight. Check connections for corrosion and clean as required.

b. Long-term. Long-term checklists for generators and exciters.

(1) General comments. The following tasks should be performed annually unless otherwise noted, following performance of short-term checks.

(2) Checklist and schedule.

(a) Coupling Lubrication. Drain lubricant, disassemble and clean the coupling annually or whenever necessary. Reassemble, using new gaskets and fresh lubricant. Refer to manufacturer's instructions for flexible coupling.

(b) Brush replacement. When brushes have worn to half their original length, replace, seat properly and adjust brush rigging tension from 2.5 to 3.6 psi on brush riding surface. Repair and replace damaged or worn brush rigging parts. Refer to manufacturer's instructions.

(c) Brush electrolysis. Electrolytic action can occur at collector ring surfaces. This action forms a greenish coating (verdigris) on brass, bronze or copper. Effects of this action can be reduced or eliminated by reversing the polarity annually or as required. Refer to manufacturer's instructions.

(d) Commutator and collector rings. Clean commutator and collector rings with vacuum. Clean oil film and dirt with approved solvent. Dry with compressed air at about 25 psi. Check for roughness, hard spots and out-of-round condition. Service commutator and collector rings as necessary following manufacturer's instructions.

(e) Rotor winding. Rotor maintenance begins with measuring and recording the insulation resistance before the unit is placed in service. Refer to manufacturer's literature for instructions. The rotor should be thoroughly cleaned annually and inspected as follows: Check the damper winding for loose bars and the connection of each bar to its ring segment. Check the joints in the ring segments between poles. Refer to manufacturer's instructions. Check clearance per manufacturer's specifications between blower and coils. Check the field coils for movement and separation. Clean dirt and oil from winding and air passages. Check condition of turn-to-turn insulation on strap field coils. Verify condition of ground insulation on pole pieces. Check all connections between field coils and lead-out connections to collector rings. Measure and record insulation resistance between field coils and ground including the collector rings. Refer to manufacturer's instructions. Check bearings and journals for damage or excessive wear. Compare micrometer readings with the manufacturer's table of wear limits. Repair or replace mechanical parts to meet these specifications. Dry out according to manufacturer's instructions. Repair insulation damage and coat with approved insulating varnish.

(f) Rotor balancing. Measure and record vibration limits of repaired unit when it is started. Refer to manufacturer's specifications for vibration limits for the specific unit. Perform static or dynamic balancing of the unit, according to instructions, if necessary.

(g) Stator winding. Measure and record insulation resistance between stator winding and ground at the machine terminals annually.

(h) Stator service. Open up the stator annually. Clean thoroughly and inspect for the following: broken, damaged, loose or missing wedges; movement or distortion of coil ends; security of all lashing and spacers; tightness of coil supports; cooling passages are open and clean; looseness of coils in slots; cracks or other damage to coil insulation; and, connections between coils and around the frame. Measure and record insulation resistance between winding and ground at the machine terminals. Compare the values with those recorded when the machine was first put in service.

(3) Checklist and schedule for solid-state exciters. Solid-state equipment does not require long-term checks. If the equipment does not function properly, refer to the manufacturer's literature for information. Repair or replace as required.

7-4. Switchgear maintenance.

Routine maintenance instructions for switchgear consist of short- and long-term checklists. Deenergize switchgear before performing maintenance. Disconnect primary and secondary sources of power.

a. Short-term. Short-term checklists for switchgear.

(1) General comments. Before performing any tasks required by the following checklist, review the station log sheets, related records, manufacturer's recommendations and NFPA-70E, Electrical Safety Requirements for Employee Workplaces.

(2) Checklist.

(a) Panels and other exterior surfaces. Panels and exterior surfaces must be kept scrupulously clean at all times.

(b) Relays and actuating mechanisms. Clean and inspect relays and actuating mechanisms monthly. Many types of relays are used. Identify the

relays such as thermal, current overload, overspeed, liquid level, lubricating oil pressure and/or flow, frequency change, etc. Refer to manufacturer's literature for inspection procedures. Verify that all connections are tight and free of corrosion.

(c) Conductors and coils. Clean and inspect conductors and coils monthly. Verify that coating of insulating varnish is in good condition (clean, smooth and polished) and there are no indications of overheating or corona arcing.

(d) Switches. Inspect switches for proper alignment, firm contacts and smooth operation monthly. Burned or pitted copper contact surfaces may be dressed with 2/0 sandpaper. Do not dress silver contacts.

(e) Circuit breakers. Trip and close circuit breakers, check for proper operation quarterly. Check time delay and freedom of movement. Refer to manufacturer's instructions.

(f) Coils and heaters. Check coils and heaters quarterly for secure mounting and circuit continuity. Check controls and thermostats for proper operation, refer to manufacturer's instructions.

(g) Contactors. Check magnet surfaces of contactors quarterly for cleanliness. Remove gun, rust or corrosion. Adjust for even contact pressure according to manufacturer's instructions.

(h) Voltage regulators. Check voltage regulators for proper operation and adjustments quarterly. Various makes and types are used. Refer to the manufacturer's literature for instructions.

b. Long- term. Long-term checklists for switchgear. Performance of tasks is related to frequency and extent of use of the auxiliary power plant.

(1) General comments. The following tasks should be performed annually unless otherwise noted, following performance of short-term checks. The procedures are general but apply primarily to draw-out equipment.

(2) Checklist and schedule.

(a) Meters and instruments. Check meters and instruments against a verified standard. Return defective or inaccurate meters and instruments to the manufacturer or designated repair location for service and calibration.

(b) Buses. Inspect 'buses and connections for signs of overheating or weakening of insulating supports. Overheating is indicated by discoloration of the busbar. Inspect insulators for cracks and/or arc tracks. Replace defective insulators. Tighten busbar and terminal connections to the proper torque value.

(c) Indicating devices and interlocks. Check indicating devices and interlocks for proper operation. Refer to manufacturer's instructions.

(d) Disconnecting devices. Check primary disconnecting device contacts for signs of overheating or abnormal wear. Clean contacts with silver polish. Clean disconnecting device contacts and apply light coating of approved lubricant.

(e) Enclosure. Verify that interior anchor bolts and structural bolts are tight. Inspect cable connections for signs of overheating. Tighten loose connections as required.

(f) Circuit breakers. Manually operate each breaker while in test position, verify proper operation. Refer to manufacturer's instructions.

(g) Environmental conditions. More frequent inspections of the switchgear must be made when unusual service conditions exist, such as contaminating fumes, excessive moisture, or extreme heat or cold. Additional protection may be required if adverse conditions are present.

(h) Ground resistance. Measure and record ground resistance values using a ground resistance test set. Compare these values with those recorded during previous tests. The tests indicate grounding system effectiveness and possible deterioration since the last tests.

CHAPTER 8

LUBRICATING OIL PURIFICATION

8-1. Purification systems.

Oil purification systems, either in the engine pressure system or oil supply system are classified by the method of flow used' in purifying the oil. The systems frequently used are the bypass and full-flow types as follows:

a. In the bypass system part of the total oil circulating in the engine passes through the filter or purifying equipment. The system continuously cleans a small portion of the oil and, in general, removes contaminants as fast as they are formed in the engine. Thus, new oil may deteriorate but will gradually stabilize when the effectiveness of the filtration system matches the rate of production of contaminants.

b. In the full-flow system all of the oil circulating in the engine passes through filtering equipment prior to going to the engine.

8-2. Forms of contamination.

Refer to appendix C paragraph C-le(2) for information on complete sample testing. Oil contamination usually occurs in one of two forms, as follows:

a. Impurities such as dirt, carbon particles or other solid matter entering the oil.

b. Undesirable substances such as water, polymerized products of oil breakdown, acids and other chemical matter entering the oil.

8-3. Methods of purifying.

Oil purification is accomplished by the use of one, or any combination, of the following methods: straining, filtering, centrifuging, or reclaiming.

a. Straining. The usual type of oil strainer can be woven wire screen or perforated sheet metal. Edge-type and wire-wound strainers are also used. The edge-type consists of stacks of metal discs separated by thin washers. The wire-wound type consists of a spool wrapped with finely serrated wire forming a clearance between adjacent wires. Strainers are designed to remove solid particles from the oil, usually between 0.0015 and 0.003 inches in size, depending on the engine manufacturer's specifications. Refer to the strainer manufacturer's literature for details and servicing instructions.

b. Filtering. Filtering is accomplished using chemically neutral or chemically activated filtering material.

(1) *Chemically neutral.* The oil filter usually consists of a canister or tank containing a chemi-

cally neutral, highly absorbent material. Cotton, cellulose waste, or paper is usually used as the absorbent filtering material. The filter tank is provided with necessary entry and exit ports, internal tubing (perforated and solid), check valves and orifices to ensure proper flow of the oil through the filtering material. Filters are more efficient than strainers in removing very small particles and are usually designed to process strained oil. Refer to the filter manufacturer's literature for details and servicing instructions.

(2) *Chemically actuated.* Absorbent filters contain chemically activated material instead of chemically neutral material. Construction of absorbent-type and adsorbent-type filters is similar. The filtering materials include charcoal, clay and fuller's earth. These materials remove water, acidic components, and may absorb certain light petroleum elements, waxes or residual products. They usually accomplish good purification and may reduce acidity as well as remove the solid contaminants. Absorbent or adsorbent filters may be used on straight run, uncompounded mineral oils where there is no danger of removing essential additives. Absorbent filters (chemically-neutral filters) should be used in conjunction with compounded or additive-type oil. Refer to the filter manufacturer's literature for details and servicing instructions. Ensure that the filtering system complies with the engine manufacturer's recommendations.

c. Centrifuging. An oil purification centrifuge usually consists of a stationary bowl that encloses a rotating element. The element, mounted on a vertically arranged axis, rotates at a high speed within the bowl. High-speed rotation causes a column of oil to form in the portion of the element nearest the center and a column of water to balance this at the outer edge of the centrifuge bowl. Solid particles having a gravity value heavier than that of the oil are thrown outward, and the heavy solids accumulate in the centrifuge bowl. Water is removed by the high gravity differential produced by the high speed of the centrifuge. Effective mechanical separation occurs; however, materials in a suspended state are not always removed by this method. Chemical contaminants are separated only if they have a markedly different specific gravity from that of the oil. Polymerized products having a gravity similar to that of oil are not separated and, in general, fuel oil dilution is not affected or corrected. The centrifuge is used extensively in fuel oil purification but has reduced application to diesel and internal combustion engine lubricants. If used in an oil reclaiming system, it is usually only a part of the total process. Refer to the manufacturer's literature for details and servicing instructions.

d. Reclaimming. Various types of oil reclaiming equipment are used. Most reclaimers operate with the oil heated at about 400°F, which drives off water vapor and lighter fuel oil dilution. Highly effective reclamation of regular mineral oil is possible. Almost complete removal of additive material occurs during reclaiming. Oils produced from a reclaimer must be limited to services not requiring an additive oil. Operation at temperatures above 400°F result in partial breakdown of the lubricating oil, which can produce an oil having a higher viscosity than the original oil. Oil reclaimers are normally used for processing oil between the impure oil and the clean oil system or may route the reclaimed oil to a separate tank for use in other lubricating services. Refer to the manufacturer's literature for details and servicing instructions.

e. Oil quality standards. Oil quality standards are provided below.

Table 8-1. Oil quality standards.

	Normal	Maximum
Water and Sediment	1.0%	5.0%
Water	0.5%	3.0%
Sediment	0.5%	2.0%

Table 8-I. Oil quality standards-Continued

	Normal	Maximum
Viscosity	±5.0%	±10.0%
Corrosion (copper strip)	None	Dull
pH	7.0% or higher	6.8%
Filtered Particles		
Larger than oil filter	None	2.0%
Metallic under 1 micron	Few	1.0%
over 5 micron	None	1.0%
(% of total residue)		

8-4. Oil maintenance procedures.

The following information is a general guide for maintenance of lubricating oil.

a. Water and sediment. Clean by centrifuging.

b. Viscosity. Treat with oil reclaimer to drive off dilution.

c. Viscosity. Centrifuge (hot) to remove heavy sludge. If necessary, add straight run mineral oil of lower viscosity.

d. Corrosion. Treat with activated-type reclaimer. If an additive oil is in use, the presence of corrosive qualities indicates that the additive is exhausted. New oil must be used if the benefit of additives is required. Used oil may be reclaimed and used for other services not requiring the additive.

e. Particles. Passage of particles larger than the filter's specifications are a definite sign of channeling or structural damage to filter elements. Replace filter cartridges.

APPENDIX A

REFERENCES

Government Publications.

AR 420-43	Facilities Engineering Electrical Services
DA PAM 738-750	Functional Users Manual for the Army Maintenance Management System (TAMMS)
MIL-STD-188-124	System Grounding Standards
NAVFAC MO-207	Operation and Maintenance of Internal Combustion Engines
TB 750-65 1	Use of Antifreeze Solutions, Antifreeze Extender, and Cleaning Compounds in Engine Cooling Systems
TM 5-682	Facilities Engineering; Electrical Facilities Safety
TM 5-683/NAVFAC MO-ll6/AFJMAN 32-1083	Facilities Engineering; Electrical Interior Facilities
TM 750-254	Cooling Systems-Tactical Vehicles
40 CFR 761	Toxic Substances Control Act

Nongovernment Publications.

American Society for Testing and Materials (ASTM):
    1916 Race St., Philadelphia, PA 19103

D-877	Dielectric Voltage Tests
D-923	Sampling Insulating Liquids
D-1524	Liquid Color Tests
D-1534	Liquid Acidity Tests

National Fire Protection Association (NFPA):
    1 Batterymarch Park, Quincy, MA 02269

NFPA 70	National Electric Code, (1993)
NFPA 70B	Recommended Practice for Electrical Equipment Maintenance, (1994)

Prescribed Form

DD Form 2744	Emergency/Auxiliary Generator Operating Log (Inspection Testing)

APPENDIX B

FUEL AND FUEL STORAGE

B-1. Diesel fuel.

Diesel fuel should comply with Federal Specifications W-F-800 MIL-F-16884, or specifications for JP-8. These specifications include grades DF-A, DF-1, DF-2 or types I and II. All are suitable for use under applicable temperature and service conditions. Different grades of fuel should not be mixed.

a. Cleanliness. Fuel must be clean. All dirt, dust, water, sediment, and other contaminants must be kept out of the fuel to prevent damage to engine fuel injection equipment. The specified grade of clean fuel must be used to ensure long, economical engine operation. Handling of fuel must be reduced to a minimum to avoid entry of contaminants. Delivery of fuel to storage tanks and then pumping it directly to the day tank through filters is a recommended procedure. Filters must be installed in all engine fuel lines and must be cleaned as recommended by the engine manufacturer.

b. Contamination. Stored fuel and fuel storage systems must be inspected at regular intervals such as every 90 days. Samples for detecting fuel contaminations are as follows:

(1) Inspect fuel filters for indication of microorganism growth, rust, scale, or sediment. In a glass jar, collect a sample of diesel fuel from the bottom of the tank. Solid contaminants will settle and collect at the bottom of the jar. Clean the filters as directed by manufacturer's instructions.

(2) Detect water in diesel fuel by collecting in a glass jar a sample of fuel from the bottom of the tank. Fuel and water will separate when the sample is allowed to settle, water will sink to the bottom of the jar. Fuel with water in it may appear white and cloudy when agitated.

(3) Detect gasoline or kerosene in diesel fuel by collecting a sample (refer to *b* above). Fuel and contaminants will separate when the sample is allowed to settle, the gasoline or kerosene will float on the fuel.

(4) Detect Oil soluble soaps in diesel fuel by having an appropriate laboratory test performed. Avoid this kind of contamination, do not use galvanized storage tanks or piping.

(5) Prevent condensation within storage tanks by keeping the tanks full. Tanks must be kept full during cold weather.

c. Storage. Fuel tanks used for storage must have drain valves for removal of bottom water (to be done

once every six months). Deterioration of stored fuel is caused by three factors: oxidation, microorganism contamination and corrosion.

(1) Oxidation occurs directly or through catalytic action. Oxygen from the air or fuel combines with fuel hydrocarbons causing oxidation. Resultant oxidation continues as long as oxygen is present. Metals suspended in the fuel act as catalysts. Metals can enter the fuel during refining, distribution or storage. The engine fuel system can thereby be damaged.

(2) Microorganism contamination is caused by bacteria and fungus that exist in the bottom water. Waste by-products of the microorganisms form a self-sustaining corrosive environment. The by-products can form a gelatinous mass which plugs fuel lines and filters, and forms a fuel sludge thereby reducing engine efficiency and possibly damaging the engine.

(3) Corrosion of the storage tank does not directly deteriorate the fuel. Corrosion can destroy a metal storage tank, usually at the bottom. Metals that enter the fuel act chemically to speed up oxidation. The combination of microorganism growth and water causes oxidation.

B-2. Gas turbine fuel.

Fuel for gas turbines consists of natural gas or light distillate oil such as kerosene or commercial jet engine fuel, Jet A or Jet A-l. All are suitable for use under applicable temperature and service conditions. Most gas turbines can burn fuels used by diesel engines. Gas and oil fuels should not be mixed.

a. Cleanliness. Fuel must be clean. All dirt, dust, water, sediment, and other contaminants must be kept out of fuel to prevent damage to engine components. Only the specified grade of clean fuel should be used to ensure reliable engine operation. Handling of fuel must be reduced to a minimum to avoid entry of contaminants. Refer to paragraph C-1*a* for information relating to cleanliness of liquid fuel. Natural gas should be passed through several fine screen filters, to remove solid particles and water vapor, before it is fed to the gas turbine engine.

b. Contamination. Stored fuel and fuel storage systems must be inspected at regular intervals such as every 90 days. Examples for detecting fuel contamination in distillate (liquid) fuels are given in paragraph C-1b(1) through (5). Perform the following checks when cleaning filters for a natural gas system.

(1) Inspect the solid particles removed by fine screen filters. Determine if the particles are dust or dirt, or the type of metal if metallic.

(2) Inspect water accumulation for acid or alkaline content.

c. *Storage.* Methods and problems for storing distillate (liquid) fuels are described in paragraph C-1c. Information relating to storing natural gas fuel follows:

(1) Natural gas can be stored in low pressure surface containers or high pressure sub-surface containers and metal bottles.

(2) Liquefied natural gas can be stored in insulated metal tanks installed as sub-surface units.

(3) The type of storage employed for natural gas depends on plant requirements and fuel availability.

B-3. Fuel storage maintenance procedures.

a. Provide the base engineer's office with the reports and results of inspections performed in paragraphs C-1c and C-2c. The base engineer will review this data and take appropriate corrective action which may include any or all of the following.

(1) Add an antioxidant to prevent oxidation or "aging" of a fuel.

(2) Add a fungicide or biocide to destroy organisms present in the water beneath stored fuel.

(3) Add a metal deactivator because metals in fuel catalyze or speed up oxidation. Inhibitors that place an amine film on metal surfaces are available. Amines are organic compounds that neutralize an electrical charge in metals.

b. Note that any chemical or additive that is added to stored fuel must be approved by the Environmental Protection Agency. Also, the base engineer's office should monitor the removal of bottom water from storage tanks (refer to para B-1c).

APPENDIX C

LUBRICATING OIL

C-1. Diesel engine oil.

Lubricating oil for diesel engines should comply with Federal Specifications MIL-L-2 104 and MIL-L-9000. Oil that complies with the specifications produces acceptable amounts of carbon residue during engine use and has acceptable pour, flash, and fire points. Straight mineral oil is the basic ingredient. Inhibitors or chemicals are added to the oil by the oil refiner to ensure compatibility with a range of engines operating under varying conditions. The user must observe recommendations by the engine manufacturer for specific types and grades of oil for optimum engine performance.

a. Characteristics. Engine lubrication requires selection of the proper oil. Refer to the engine manufacturer instructions. Examples of required oil characteristics are as follows:

(1) Oil should have sufficient viscosity to prevent metal-to-metal contact. Oils with lower SAE numbers are lighter and flow more readily than oils with higher numbers. Heavier oils, those with higher SAE numbers, may cause sluggish operation and power loss.

(2) Oil should remain stable during use under changing temperatures and conditions for satisfactory service.

(3) Check the engine periodically, such as every six months, for accumulation of sludge in the engine filters and strainers and around valve springs. Refer to the engine manufacturer's literature for specific information.

(4) Oil must be free of water and sediment. Collect a sample of oil in a glass jar. Allow the sample to settle. Water and solid contaminants settle to the bottom of the jar.

b. Additives. Straight mineral oil does not have detergent qualities. Therefore, various compounds are added to the oil. These additives keep the engine clean by controlling varnish formation or resisting chemical changes to reduce oxidation. Other additives form a protective film against corrosive acids.

c. Mixing oils. Different refineries may use different types of additives or certain characteristics of the mineral oil may vary. Mixing types of oil may change the necessary detergent actions. To obtain maximum benefit from additive type oils do not mix them with straight mineral oil. Concentrations of the additives is reduced when detergent oils and straight oils are mixed.

d. Changing oil. Lubricating oil must be changed periodically. Refer to recommendations by the engine manufacturer to specific conditions, time intervals, and instructions. General oil change procedures are as follows:

(1) Operate the engine before draining old oil. Oil should be drained while warm and immediately after engine shut down because contaminants are in suspension and will drain readily.

(2) Obtain a sample of the drained oil and deliver it to the base engineer for testing. Drained oil should be examined for fuel dilution, acidity, and presence of solids and other contaminants. Testing helps establish the overall condition of the engine and approximate frequency of need for oil changes.

(3) Observe the viscosity of drained oil. In diesel engines oil viscosity increases during service due to the gradual oxidation of the oil. Viscosity decreases if fuel gets into the oil by passing the piston rings or through leaks.

e. Oil *analysis program.*

(1) Personnel in the engineer's office, and other cognizant personnel, should refer to the Army Oil Analysis Program (AOAP) for sampling and analysis information. The program is described in TB 43-0210.

(2) The analysis of periodic samples of the lubricating oil should report the character and amount of contaminants, wear metals and additives in the oil. However, some amounts of wear metals and contaminants will have been collected by the chip collectors, strainers, filters, separators of the system and also as sludge. To secure the total picture it is necessary to analyze all such collected material to determine the total rate of increase/decrease of each. This will indicate what has occurred during the period between samples.

(3) The prudent responsible operator will log and use all such data to track trends that give warning of conditions that may result, if uncorrected, in major problems.

C-2. Gas turbine oil.

Lubricating oil for gas turbines should comply with Federal Specifications MIL-L-23699 or MIL-L-7808. Oil that complies with the specification can withstand the high temperatures encountered during engine operation.

a. Additives. Various compounds are added to mineral oil to provide the special characteristics required for use in gas turbines. The user must observe lubricating oil recommendations by the engine manufacturer for optimum engine performance.

b. Changing oil Refer to the engine manufacturer's literature for recommendations related to specific conditions, time intervals, and instructions for changing the lubricating oil.

(1) Collect a sample of old oil when oil is drained from the engine storage tank. Examine the drain plug or valve, filter, and chip detector if used, for metal particles. Save the particles for analysis.

(2) Deliver the drain oil sample and particles to the base engineer for tests and analysis. The presence of some particles in the drain oil is usually considered normal by the engine manufacturer.

(3) Refer to the manufacturer's literature. An oil analysis program is usually recommended, including a spectrometric analysis of the metal particles. It is necessary to collect and evaluate data for type and quantity of engine wear-metals. Study of this data shows trends of engine wear and expected future reliability.

APPENDIX D

COOLING SYSTEMS AND COOLANTS

D-1. Coolant.

The coolant used in diesel engines usually consists of a mixture of ethylene glycol antifreeze, corrosion inhibitor, and fresh water. When the engine is used in an extremely cold area, such as Arctic regions, a special antifreeze mixture is used. Specifications related to the mixtures are as follows:

Antifreeze, Ethylene glycol	MIL-A-46 153
Antifreeze, Arctic- type	MIL-A-11755
Inhibitor, Corrosion	O-1-490

The specification for cooling system cleaning compound is MIL-C-10597.

D-2. Engine water treatment.

The prime consideration in a closed water cooling system is proper water treatment to ensure no corrosion or scale occurs during static or dynamic engine conditions.

a. Acceptable conditions. In most modern diesel engines the following cooling water conditions are acceptable:

(1) pH 8.5 to 10
(2) Chloride and Sulfate   100 ppm
(3) Total Dissolved Solids   500 ppm
(4) Total Hardness   200 ppm

b. Softened water. If possible softened water should be utilized to reduce the total hardness level of the engine cooling loop. The use of softened water will increase engine performance by reducing the precipitation of calcium and magnesium at elevated temperature conditions, ensuring higher heat transfer rates.

c. Antifreeze. Typically, engine cooling systems incorporate antifreeze solutions which inhibit scale and protect the cooling system when temperatures are encountered below freezing. Ethylene glycol mixed with a corrosion inhibitor such as triazoles form an inhibiting film on metal surfaces that acts as a barrier in the corrosion process. The following concentration curves should be utilized when adding glycol solutions to engine cooling system.

d. Concentration. As indicated by the chart the concentration should exceed 30 percent. If more than 60 percent of solution is added two effects will be realized; first a decrease in heat transfer rates, second a lowering of the system freeze protection.

D-3. Cooling system maintenance.

Maintenance consists of periodically testing the antifreeze, inspecting the coolant for cleanliness, and flushing or cleaning the system with compound when necessary. Engines used in Arctic regions are covered in paragraph D-4.

a. Testing antifreeze. Perform tests to verify freeze protection and reserve alkalinity.

(1) Test for freeze protection using the combination antifreeze and battery tester, stock number 6630-00-105-1418. Instructions for using the tester are included with it.

(2) Test for reserve alkalinity (corrosion protection) using the reserve alkalinity test kit, stock number 6630-00-169-1506.

(3) Cooling systems with freeze protection below - 7 degrees F (-22 degrees C) that fail the reserve alkalinity test may be replenished with corrosion inhibitor, stock number 6850-00-753-4967. Replenishment is a one-time service. If the reserve alkalinity test is failed again, replace the coolant. If the system passes the test, record the date.

b. Inspecting coolant.

(1) Inspect the coolant visually for cleanliness. Obtain a coolant sample and place it in a clean glass container. After allowing about five minutes for settling, examine the sample for contamination (rust, foreign particles, and/or sediment). The sample may have some color (same color as original antifreeze) and should be clear.

(2) Examine the sample to determine the type and quantity of contamination. Rust, a chemical combination of iron, water, and air, is frequently found. The presence of rubber particles usually indicates deterioration of hoses. Replacement hoses may be indicated. Sediment may be caused by impurities in the water used in the coolant. Contaminants in the coolant can clog a radiator or heat exchanger and cause engine and generating system breakdown.

c. Cleaning the system. Clean the cooling system whenever the coolant is drained. Usually the system requires nothing more than thorough flushing out with fresh water. Refer to the engine manufacturer's literature for instructions. If any part of the system is rusted or partially clogged, it is necessary to use cooling system cleaning compound and conditioner, stock number 6850-00-598-7328. Do not use the compound as a routine maintenance procedure. Instructions for using the compound are included with it.

D-4. Filling the cooling system.

Refer to the engine manufacturer's literature for instructions on filling the cooling system. This is applicable to either new systems or those just cleaned and serviced.

a. Cooling system protection is required for all liquid cooled diesel engines. In areas where temperatures no lower than -55 degrees F (-48 degrees C) are expected, prepare a solution according to the table D-l below. When temperatures below freezing are not expected, use a weak solution such as one pint of ethylene glycol antifreeze for each gallon of solution for general protection against rust build up and scale formation with the engine.

b. Use arctic-type antifreeze in areas where temperatures below -55 degrees F (-48 degrees C) are expected.

c. Do not dilute arctic-type antifreeze with water or inhibitor. It is ready for use as issued.

Table D-l. Antifreeze solutions.

GUIDE FOR PREPARATION OF ETHYLENE
GLYCOL ANTIFREEZE SOLUTIONS

Lowest Estimated Temperature in Area	Pints of Antifreeze Needed to Prepare 1-Gallon of Solution
+20°F (-7°C)	1.50
+10°F (-12°C)	2.00
0°F (-18°C)	2.75
-10°F (-23°C)	3.25
-20°F (-29°C)	3.50
-30°F (-34°C)	4.00
-40°F (-40°C)	4.25
-50°F (-46°C)	4.50
-55°F (-48°C)	4.75

APPENDIX E

SAFETY

E-1. General.

The base engineer and his representatives are responsible for general safety conditions, for enforcement of safety rules, and for the condition and use of all protective devices. The base engineer is responsible for the competency of his representatives.

E-2. Safe operation.

Safe operational practices must be followed to prevent injury to personnel and damage to equipment. These practices are applicable to diesel engines, gas turbines, and generators including associated electrical equipment. Protective devices include carbon dioxide fire extinguishers and first aid kits. Whenever carbon dioxide extinguishers are used, enter the area where used cautiously. Make sure the area has been ventilated thoroughly before entering. Never use water to extinguish a fire in the engine, generator, or associated electrical equipment.

a. Diesel engines. The engine operator must perform the following visual checks before and during operation.

(1) Make sure engine coolant is at the proper level and has the proper amount of antifreeze. Check hoses for good condition.

(2) Make sure engine air requirements for combustion are met. Check air filters and cleaners for cleanliness and good condition.

(3) Make sure the engine, generator, and related equipment are clean. Keep oil-soaked rags out of the generating facility to avoid a fire hazard.

(4) Guard against accidental or unintentional starting when work is being done on the engine or associated equipment. Attach an approved safety clearance tag such as DA Form 4324 to the starting control when work is being done.

(5) Make sure engine lubricant and fuel are at the proper levels.

b. Gas turbines. The engine operator must be alert for the presence of health and fire hazards. Make sure the generating facility is well ventilated when using cleaning solvents. The following requirements must be met when the engine room is entered.

(1) The gas turbine shall be shut down or limited to idle power.

(2) The enclosure door shall be kept open. If the gas turbine is operating, station an observer at the enclosure door.

(3) Do not touch any part of an operating engine, as the engine becomes extremely hot. Wear insulated gloves as necessary.

(4) Wear approved ear protection if the engine is operating.

(5) Do not remain in the room or enclosure, or in the plane of rotation, when starting or monitoring the engine.

(6) Attach an approved safety clearance tag such as DA Form 4324 to the starting control when work is being done.

(7) Make sure the engine, generator, and related equipment are clean. Keep oil-soaked rags out of the generating facility to avoid a fire hazard.

c. Generators. Personnel must be familiar with recommendations and procedures described in TM 5-682.

E-3. Electrical safety.

a. General. All operating must be familiar with the following general safety precautions.

(1) Do not rely on safety devices. Never assume power is off or disconnected. Use and/or look for a safety clearance tag before working on high voltage equipment.

(2) Use rubber gloves, with valid "usefulness" certification, when working on equipment or transmission lines.

(3) Stand on good rubber mat when working on generator equipment or switchgear.

(4) Have a person qualified in first aid for electrical shock present at all times when working.

b. Rescue of shock victims.

(1) Protect yourself with dry insulating material.

(2) Open the circuit, wear rubber gloves to pull the victim away from the live conductor. Do not touch the victim with bare hands until the circuit is open.

c. First aid. Look for hemorrhage, stoppage of breathing, wounds, fractures, etc. Indications of shock include: pale face, clammy and sweaty conditions, weakness, and a weak and rapid pulse. Do the following in any emergency.

(1) Send for a doctor or carry the victim to a doctor.

(2) Make sure the victim is comfortable. Keep the victim warm, quiet, and flat on the back.

(3) Loosen the victim's clothing. If breathing has stopped, apply artificial resuscitation. Study the procedures in TM 5-682, Section VIII. Do not

wait until an emergency requiring aid occurs, know what to do.

(4) Treat serious bleeding and stoppage of breathing in that order before anything else is done.

(5) Feel for the patient's pulse. Failure to find a pulse does not indicate death. Immediately begin artificial resuscitation. Continue until the doctor arrives.

APPENDIX F

RECORDS

F-1. Manufacturer's forms.

Manufacturers provide specific instructions for the use and care of their products. Very often these instructions include forms and log sheets for record keeping on an hourly or daily basis for continuously operating engines and generators.

F-2. DD Form 2744 (Emergency/Auxiliary Generator Operation log).

Use DD Form 2744 for inspection testing of emergency/auxiliary generators. Enter readings immediately after start and prior to shut-down. If the engine runs more than one hour, record every two hours with a minimum of two readings. Use the form to record system performance during inspection and testing. Record information such as operating data, condition of lube oil (viscosity test), condition of plant and subsystems, deficiencies and

corrective measures. This data helps determine the need for further maintenance. Supervisors can develop a local checklist and use it for inspections not requiring generator operations. Complete a DD Form 2744 for each scheduled emergency or auxiliary generator exercise. When possible, fill out the forms during unscheduled power outages. During extended generator operations, check generators as frequently as manpower and scheduling permit. Only one form is necessary for each event. Annotate each check on the back of the form, to assist in troubleshooting if a problem arises between checks. The workcenter should keep completed forms for quick reference. If desired, place a second copy on the unit in a protective cover. The supervisor responsible for maintaining emergency/auxiliary generators and associated equipment must review completed forms periodically.

EMERGENCY/AUXILIARY GENERATOR OPERATING LOG (INSPECTION TESTING)

1. ENGINE DATA

a. MAKE CATERPILLAR	b. MODEL D.3200
c. SERIAL NUMBER 185165	d. RPM 1800

e. HOUR METER 2000	(1) START 2000	(2) FINISH 2001

f. INSPECTION TEST OPERATOR JOE SPARKS	g. DATE 5/15/96
h. BASE/POST FORT TANK	i. UNIT 535 TH

2. ALTERNATOR DATA

a. MAKE KATO	b. MODEL 2380
c. SERIAL NUMBER	d. KW RATING 500 KW
e. VOLTS 480	f. PHASE 3φ
g. SHOP SUPERVISOR JOHN PUNCH	h. DATE; 5/20/96
i. LOCATION (Building) 350	J. RECORD IDENT NUMBER 96S2009

3. GENERAL CONDITIONS (See Note 7)

	S	U	N	REMARKS
a. CLEANLINESS	√			
b. EXHAUST CONDITION	√			
c. ENGINE VIBRATION	√			
d. LOOSE ITEMS (Bolts, Linkage, etc. J		√		FAN BELT IS LOOSE
e. TURBO VIBRATION	√			

f. WATER LEAKS (X) X YES ___ NO	g. LOCATION OF LEAK AT COOLING PUMP

4. FUEL SYSTEM (See Note 7)

	S	U	N	REMARKS
a. FUEL LEVEL (Day Tank)	√			
b. FUEL LEVEL [Storage Tank)	√			

c. WATER DRAINED (X) ___ YES X NO	d. FUEL LEAKS (X) ___ YES X NO
e. LOCATION OF LEAK	

5. BATTERY BANK (See Note 7)

	S	U	N	REMARKS,
a. CONNECTIONS		√		LOOSE CONNECTION
b. CLEANLINESS		√		BATTERY TERMINALS SHOULD BE CLEANED
c. ELECTROLYTE LEVEL	√			

6. VOLTAGE REGULATOR (See Note 1)

	S	U	N	REMARKS
a. REGULATOR MOUNTS	√			
b. RHEOSTAT CONDITION (Corroded, connections, etc.	√			

7. AUTOMATIC TRANSFER PANEL (See Note 1)

	S	U	N	REMARKS
a. CONTACTS BURNED	√			
b. MECHANISM BINDING	√			
c. WIRING DAMAGED	√			
d. COMPONENTS OVERHEATED	√			

8. COOLING SYSTEM (See Note 2)

a. TEMP. DURING STANDBY 70° F	b. TEMP. DURING OPERATIONS 130°F
c. COOLANT ADDED (Level) FULL	d. ANTIFREEZE PROTECTION (See Note 3) -5°F
e. FAN BELT CONDITION OK	f. RADIATOR AND LOUVER CONDITION OK

9. LUBE OIL SYSTEM

a. OIL CHANGED (X) X YES ___ NO	b. OIL ADDED (Sum level) X YES ___ NO
c. LUBE OIL CONDITION (Viscosity)	d. LEVEL IN GOVERNOR OK

ITEM (See Note 2J	ALTERNATOR	EXCITER
10. KW LOAD	350	

		PH1	PH2	PH3
11. AMPERAGE		420	415	410
12. VOLTAGE		480	480	480

13. BRUSHES AND BRUSHES RIGGING	
14. SLIP RING CONDITION	
15. COMMUTATOR CONDITION	

16. VOLTAGE (Commercial)	PH1 480	PH2 480	PH3 480

17. BATTERY CHARGER	
a. VOLTS 125 VDC	b. AMPS 15

18. HYDROMETER READING	19. STARTING AIR (Psi)	20. AMBIENT TEMP. (°F) 75

21. FILTER CHANGE

a. LUBE OIL (X) X YES ___ NO	b. FUEL (X) X YES ___ NO	c. AIR INTAKE (X) ___ YES ___ NO

22. UNIT STARTED ON (X)

___ 1ST TRY	X 2ND TRY	___ 3RD TRY	___ NOT AT ALL

Use the reverse side of this form and/or 8-l /2 x 11" paper if required for additional comments, continuation of item entries (identify by item number), and for corrective action(s) taken.
NOTE 1: Mark S for Satisfactory, U for Unsatisfactory, N for Normal, or indicate in Remarks column, as applicable.
NOTE 2: Enter data as indicated. Where no instrumentation is provided, indicate Satisfactory, Unsatisfactory, etc., as applicable.
NOTE 3: Enter Antifreeze Protection as the freeze temperature in degrees (F) as indicated on an appropriate hydrometer.

DD FORM 2744, MAY 96   LOCAL REPRODUCTION AUTHORIZED.

Figure F-1. Sample DD Form 2744 (Emergency /Auxiliary Generator Operating Log

Enter readings immediately after start-up and prior to shut-down. If engine runs more than one hour, record every two hours with minimum of two readings.

23. UNIT TYPE

a. MODEL	b. REGISTRATION NO.
2380	16720

24. ALTERNATOR

a. KW RATING	b. VOLTS	c. FREQUENCY
500	480	60

25. ENGINE READINGS

DATE a.	TIME b.	HOUR METER c.	OIL PRESSURE d.	WATER TEMP. e.	FUEL LEVEL f.	EXHAUST CON/TEM g.	KW LOAD h.	i. VOLTS PH1	i. VOLTS PH12	i. VOLTS PH3	c. FREQUENCY	j. AMPS PH1	j. AMPS PH2	j. AMPS PH3	BATTERY CHARGER AMPS k.	PRINTED NAME AND SIGNATURE l.
5/3/96	0800	2000	60	225 F	FULL	1350 F	350	480	460	480	60	420	415	410	15	JOE SPARKS Joe Sparks

26. COMMENTS

DD FORM 2744 (BACK), MAY 96

Figure F-1. Sample DD Form 2744 (Emergency/Auxiliary Generator Operating Log (page 2)

APPENDIX G

DIESEL ENGINES: OPERATION, TIMING, AND TUNING INSTRUCTIONS

G-1. Starting and stopping.

a. General. Starting and stopping procedures apply to diesel engines that are not equipped with an automatic start and shutdown feature such as the manually operated engine used in a Class B system. The procedures may be used if an engine is to be exercised. Instructions for the operator, including operation and recording of instrument data, are provided.

b. Starting. Before starting make sure engine ancillary equipment is ready to function. The major portion of normal wear occurs while starting a cold engine or an engine which has been idle. Proper starting technique includes inspection to verify that the engine and its accessory plant are ready for operation, adequate fuel is available, and lubricating oil, coolant and other supplies are at proper levels. Starting involves proper positioning of the engine, use of the starting system and proper acceleration to operating speed. Starting also includes application of the load to the engine.

c. Operation. After engine operation starts and the load is applied, operator duties include following the load variations and making necessary operational adjustments. The operator must continuously observe operation to determine deviations from normal or acceptable including ranges of operating pressures, temperatures or other operational parameters. Unusual sounds, smells, vibrations of oscillations of the engine and major variations in instrument readings, may indicate some abnormal condition.

d. Recording. Instrument readings and operator observations must be recorded for analysis. These data may indicate trends toward deterioration or need for adjustment. Entries on engine and related logs must be at regular intervals and accurate.

e. Operational maintenance. The operator should be alert to possible malfunctions or deviations during operation. Operational adjustments such as pressure and temperature should be noted and recorded, if unusual. Ancillary equipment must be inspected during engine operation.

f. Stopping. Proper technique in stopping the engine and shutting down the ancillary equipment is necessary. Correct shutdown permits the engine to cool without excessive distortion of parts or stresses being imposed. The engine will be ready for restart and subsequent use when needed. An engine can be damaged by improper shutdown or starting practices.

G-2. Engine timing.

a. Timing function. The fuel injection system must be timed so that combustion starts at, or just before, piston top dead center (TDC).

(1) Early ignition produces excessively high cylinder pressures and detonation from the rapid pressure rise. Late ignition occurs when the piston is moving away from the cylinder head, consequently the expansion ratio is reduced and efficiency is lost. Another timing function is the rate of injection, or the duration of the injection period.

(2) Injection continues over a measurable period of time, usually expressed in degrees of crankshaft rotation. It is desirable to inject the fuel as quickly as possible without creating high cylinder pressures. The fuel burning period should be completed within the 15-20 degrees of crankshaft rotation after top dead center.

(3) The time of start of injection is determined by ignition delay, since initial combustion must be secured by top dead center, or slightly before. Duration of the injection period is determined by the allowable rate of pressure rise in the cylinder. If ignition delay is assumed to be .0025 second, the following applies to high, medium and low speed engines operating at 1,800,600 and 300 rpm respectively.

Table G-1. Ignition delay and duration.

	ENGINE SPEED		
Description	High	Medium	Low
Engine RPM	1.800	600	300
Revolutions/second	30	10	5
Degrees/second	10,800	3,600	1,800
Ignition delay. degrees	27	9	4.5
Probable duration, degrees	30	20	15

(4) Note that the high-speed engine would require an injection start timing 27 to 30 degrees before top dead center, and that all fuel is in the cylinder by 3 degrees after top dead center. Pressure rise is rapid once ignition starts, because nearly all of the fuel is in the cylinder. As speed is reduced, a later start of injection is possible. For the speed engine, about half of the total fuel charge is in the cylinder when ignition occurs, but the balance of the charge is injected into the burning portion.

(5) For the low-speed engine, about one-third of the fuel charge is present, while two-thirds of the charge is injected at a controlled rate after ignition occurs. In practice, the lower speed engines use a lower octane fuel. Since such engines are usually large, a relatively coarse atomization is used, resulting in greater ignition delay. In low-speed engines, actual fuel timing is usually in the range from 7 to 12 degrees before top dead center.

(6) The medium-speed engines usually are timed from 10 to 18 degrees before top dead center while high-speed units will range as much as 35 to 40 degrees before top dead center. Generally, the duration of injection decreases with speed.

b. *Timing procedure.* Timing is established by setting the fuel injection cam with the control system in the maximum fuel position. Since the fuel cam is usually symmetrical, lost motion affects the opening and closing times equally. For example, if an engine were timed at full load for opening 10 degrees before top dead center and closing 10 degrees after top dead center, at half load, the timing might be 6 degrees before top dead center to 6 degrees after top dead center. By lowering fuel pressure, the injection period can be lengthened to approach the full load values. Balance is secured by adjusting the lost motion device for each of the cylinders. It is important to maintain all fuel nozzle tips in good condition, and to have carefully matched orifices on the nozzle. The nozzle orifice and duration of injection are the only balancing adjustments. Since duration should be similar for all cylinders, matched orifices must be used. Always install new fuel nozzle orifices in full sets for a common rail engine.

G-3. Engine tuning.

a. *General* Tuning of diesel engines is necessary whenever the engine is not running normally, has lost power, or has operated the number of hours that constitute a tune-up interval.

b. *Tune-up categories.* There are two categories of tune-up, minor and major. Refer to the time interval specified by the manufacturer for minor and major tune-ups. The specific manufacturer's literature should be consulted for tune up details related to the engine in use.

(1) Minor tune-up includes the following:

(a) Retorque cylinder head. This is optional; follow manufacturer's instructions.

(b) Adjust tappet clearance.

(c) Adjust injector timing or setting on engine using unit injectors.

(d) Check pump static timing on engines using a pump-nozzle combination.

(e) Change fuel filters and strainers.

(f) Check air filter. Change air filter oil if oil bath type.

(g) Check high idle speed.

(h) Check low idle speed

(i) Check engine for correct horsepower. Use dynamometer.

(j) Visually check engine for leaks.

(k) In addition to these items, some engines may require additional adjustment or checking before the tune-up is complete.

(2) Major tune-up includes the following:

(a) Retorque cylinder head.

(b) Adjust tappet clearance.

(c) Clean and adjust injectors and/or injection nozzles.

(d) Check pump static timing.

(e) Change fuel filters and strainers. Drain engine coolant.

(f) Service air cleaner.

(g) Check and overhaul injection pump if needed.

(h) Check high idle speed.

(i) Check low idle speed.

(j) Check engine for correct horsepower. Use dynamometer

(k) Visually check engine for leaks.

(3) During the tune-up, check for any loose bolts or hose clamps that may be a potential trouble spot. Also, replace all gaskets, such as tappet cover gaskets, pump gaskets, timing cover gaskets, and any other gaskets that have been disturbed during the tune-up.

G-4. Engine failure and repairs.

a. *Failure identification.* A well planned and executed preventive maintenance program reduces the possibilities of experiencing a catastrophic engine failure. However, it is not completely possible to prevent or anticipate such a failure. Indication of some of these failures are as follows:

(1) *Crankcase explosions.* If, during operation, explosions can be heard in the crankcase, shut the engine down immediately. Allow the engine to cool before removing any cover plates for inspection.

(2) *Runaway engine.* May be caused by a stuck fuel pump rack or defective engine safety stop. Lubricate the control linkage when the engine is at rest or shut off the fuel supply to the engine, as necessary.

(3) *Sudden stop.* May be caused by overload, low lubricating oil, seized engine components, or empty fuel tank. Inspect to identify the problem. Allow the engine to cool before removing any cover plates.

(4) *Unusual noises.* Can be caused by fuel injection equipment troubles, a loose or broken con-

necting rod, faulty piston rings or wrist pins, or a loose flywheel. Inspect to identify the problem.

b. Repairs. Repairs must be prompt and thorough to restore the engine to serviceable condition as rapidly as possible. Such repairs normally depend on the immediate repair parts inventory but may also require maximum ingenuity in producing a useable repair part. Particular attention must be given to not only the part which failed, but also to all other parts which might be affected by the failure. Merely replacing an obviously defective part often will lead to a series of diffi-culties originating from by-products or effects of the initial failure. Therefore, carefully check all of the related and resultant functions of the faulty part or any other component affected by it to make sure that the engine has been thoroughly restored to operable condition. For example, if a connecting rod bearing fails, replace the bearing and examine the crank journal to see if it has been scored or damaged and if all oil passages to the piston are properly clear. Also, verify that connecting rod bolts or adjacent main bearings have not been affected.

GLOSSARY

Section I
Abbreviations

A, AMP
amperes

AC
alternating current

AS
ammeter switch

BDC
bottom dead center

C
Centigrade

CFM
cubic feet per minute

CFR
Code of Federal Regulation

CI
compression ignition

CPT
control power transformer

CT
current transformer

DC
direct current

EMF
electromotive force

F
Fahrenheit

FU
fuse

HP
horsepower

HPT
high pressure turbine

Hz
hertz

IR
infrared

kVAR, kilovars
kilo volt amperes reactance

kVA
kilo volt amperes

kv
kilo volts

kw
kilo watts

LPT
low pressure turbine

NEMA
National Electrical Manufacturers Association

NFPA
National Fire Protection Association

PCB
polychlorinated biphenyls

PH
pouvior hydrogene

PPM
parts per million

psi
pounds per square inch

PT
potential transformer

RFI
radio frequency interference

RPM
revolutions per minute

RTD
resistance temperature detector

SI
spark ignition

TDC
top dead center

UPS
uninterruptible power supply

V
volt

VAR
volt amperes reactance

VM
voltmeter

VOM
volt ohm milliammeter

vs
voltmeter switch

W
watt

WHDM
watt-hour demand meter

WM

Section II
Terms

Alternating current
An electric current that is continually varying in value and reversing its direction of flow at regular intervals. A cycle is one complete set of positive and negative values of an alternating current. The number of cycles occurring in one second (cycles per second or Hertz) is called frequency. Alternating current voltage is expressed as volts AC.

Brayton cycle
The operating principle by which a gas turbine engine operates, called constant pressure combustion.

Charge (circuit breaker)
The loading or tensioning of circuit breaker springs by compression and/or extension.

Circuit breaker
A device for closing and/or interrupting a circuit without damage to itself or the equipment it is protecting when properly applied within its rating. The interruption feature of this device functions when an abnormal condition such as an overload or short circuit occurs. The device usually is set to trip at 125 percent of full load current.

Dew point
Dew point is the temperature at which dew starts to form (vapor condenses into liquid).

Direct current
An electric current that flows continually in one direction. Direct current voltage is expressed as volts DC.

Electromotive force
The potential, or voltage, developed by a dynamo or battery.

Emergency power
A power source (held in reserve) that is available for use in the event of failure of the normal power source. Transfer to and/or from emergency power can be automatic or manual.

Fault current
Current flowing to a fault. It may be leakage, a short circuit, or a direct ground.

Four cycle (four stroke) engine
A reciprocating (piston) engine, using gasoline or diesel oil for fuel. The engine produces one power impulse per cylinder for every four strokes of the piston. One stroke is one pass through the cylinder.

Fuel filter
Device used to separate solids, impurities, and water from the fuel.

Gear pump
Delivers fuel from tank to injectors.

Governor
A mechanism used to control the speed of an engine.

Governor characteristics
Terms used in discussion of a governor:

a. Governor sensitivity. Ability to detect a change in engine speed, expressed as percent of rated top speed.

b. Governor speed droop. Change in engine speed as load increases, expressed as percent of rated speed.

c. Governor reset. Adjustment to the governor (internal or external) which changes the set speed at any given load point.

d. Isochronous governor. A governor with automatic reset which compensates for speed droop. Constant engine speed is maintained regardless of load.

e. Governor output. Measure of power the governor can provide to activate the fuel control mechanism. Expressed in pounds per inch or pounds per foot.

Grounding
Grounding is the connection of a low resistance metallic conductor between the power distribution system's neutral lead and earth (or an equivalent conducting body). Grounding safely clears line-to-ground faults.

Hertz
A unit of frequency equal to one cycle per second (refer to alternating current).

Hunting
Periodic increase and decrease (oscillation) in speed, voltage, or other quantity.

Injector
Meters, times, and pressurizes fuel to be delivered to the cylinder.

Magnetism

Property of certain materials which exerts a mechanical force, attraction or repulsion, on an adjacent mass of similar materials.

Otto cycle

The operating principle by which a piston (reciprocating) engine operates, called constant volume combustion.

Polychlorinated biphenyls

PCB, a liquid with high dielectric strength that was used as an insulator in power transformers, relays, circuit breakers, etc.

Scavenging

The removal of exhaust (burned) gases from the cylinders of a piston (reciprocating) engine. Also, refers to the collection and removal of excess lubricating oil from a bearing housing in a gas turbine engine.

Supercharge

A method of increasing the volume of air charge in the cylinders of piston engines to produce higher power output. A belt or chain driven blower is used to supercharge an engine.

Switchgear

General term, covers switching and interrupting devices including their associated control, instrumentation, metering, protective devices, and housing. Used relative to generation, transmission, distribution, and conversion of electric power.

Tachometer

Instrument that measures angular speed, such as that of a rotating prime mover shaft. Tachometers covered herein usually use a magnetic pick-up to sense speed.

Two-cycle (two-stroke) engine

A reciprocating (piston) engine using diesel oil for fuel. The engine produces one power impulse per cylinder for every two strokes of the piston. One stroke is one pass through the cylinder.

Turbocharge

A method of increasing the volume of air charge in the cylinders of piston engines to produce higher power output. Flow of exhaust gases operates a turbocharger.

Voltage regulator

A device which controls the output voltage of a generator.

INDEX

EMERGENCY/AUXILIARY GENERATOR OPERATING LOG (INSPECTION TESTING)

1. ENGINE DATA			
a. MAKE	b. MODEL		
c. SERIAL NUMBER	d. RPM		
e. HOUR METER	(1) START	(2) FINISH	
f. INSPECTION TEST OPERATOR		g. DATE	
h BASE/POST		i. UNIT	

2. ALTERNATOR DATA		
a. MAKE	b. MODEL	
c. SERIAL NUMBER	d. KW RATING	
e. VOLTS	f. PHASE	
g. SHOP SUPERVISOR		h. DATE
i. LOCATION (Building)	j. RECORD IDENT NUMBER	

3. GENERAL CONDITIONS (See Note 1)	S	U	N	REMARKS
a. CLEANLINESS				
b EXHAUST CONDITION				
c. ENGINE VIBRATION				
d. LOOSE ITEMS (Bolts. Linkage, etc.)				
e. TURBO VIBRATION				

f. WATER LEAKS (X)		g. LOCATION OF LEAK
YES	NO	

4. FUEL SYSTEM (See Note 1)	S	U	N	REMARKS
a. FUEL LEVEL (Day Tank)				
b. FUEL LEVEL (Storage Tank)				

c. WATER DRAINED (X)		d. FUEL LEAKS (X)	
YES	NO	YES	NO

e. LOCATION OF LEAK

5. BATTERY BANK (See Note 1)	S	U	N	REMARKS
a. CONNECTIONS				
b. CLEANLINESS				
c. ELECTROLYTE LEVEL				

6. VOLTAGE REGULATOR (See Note 1)	S	U	N	REMARKS
a. REGULATOR MOUNTS				
b. RHEOSTAT CONDITION (Corroded, connections, etc.				

7. AUTOMATIC TRANSFER PANEL (See Note 1)	S	U	N	REMARKS
a. CONTACTS BURNED				
b. MECHANISM BINDING				
c. WIRING DAMAGED				
d. COMPONENTS OVERHEATED				

8. COOLING SYSTEM (See Note 2)	
a. TEMP. DURING STANDBY'	b. TEMP. DURING OPERATIONS
c. COOLANT ADDED (Level)	d. ANTIFREEZE PROTECTION (See Note 3)
e. FAN BELT CONDITION	f. RADIATOR AND LOUVER CONDITION

9. LUBE OIL SYSTEM		
a. OIL CHANGED (X)	b. OIL ADDED (Sum level)	
YES NO	YES	NO
c. LUBE OIL CONDITION (Viscosity)	d. LEVEL IN GOVERNOR	

ITEM (See Note 2)	ALTERNATOR			EXCITER
10. KW LOAD				
11. AMPERAGE	PH1	PH2	PH3	
12. VOLTAGE	PH1	PH2	PH3	
13. BRUSHES AND BRUSHES RIGGING				
14. SLIP RING CONDITION				
16. COMMUTATOR CONDITION				
16. VOLTAGE (Commercial)	PH1	PH2	PH3	

17. BATTERY CHARGER		
a. VOLTS	b. AMPS	

18. HYDROMETER READING	19. STARTING AIR (Psi)	20. AMBIENT TEMP. (°F)

21. FILTER CHANGE		
a. LUBE OIL (X)	b. FUEL (X)	c. AIR INTAKE (X)
YES NO	YES NO	YES NO

22. UNIT STARTED ON (X)			
1ST TRY	2ND TRY	3RD TRY	NOT AT ALL

Use the reverse side of this form and/or 8-I /2 x 1 1" paper if required for additional comments, continuation of item entries (identify by item number), and for corrective action(s) taken.
NOTE 1: Mark S for Satisfactory, U for Unsatisfactory, N for Normal, or indicate in Remarks column, as applicable.
NOTE 2: Enter data as indicated. Where no instrumentation is provided, indicate Satisfactory, Unsatisfactory, etc., as applicable.
NOTE 3: Enter Antifreeze Protection as the freeze temperature in degrees (F) as indicated on an appropriate hydrometer.

DD FORM 2744. MAY 96   LOCAL REPRODUCTION AUTHORIZED.

23. UNIT TYPE

a. MODEL

b. REGISTRATION NO.

24. ALTERNATOR

a. KW RATING | b. VOLTS | c. FREQUENCY

Enter readings immediately after start-up and prior to shut-down. If engine runs more than one hour, record every two hours with minimum of two readings.

25. ENGINE READINGS

DATE a.	TIME b.	HOUR METER c.	OIL PRESSURE d.	WATER TEMP e.	FUEL LEVEL f.	EXHAUST CON/TEM g.	KW LOAD h.	i. VOLTS			j. AMPS			BATTERY CHARGER AMPS k.	PRINTED NAME AND SIGNATURE l.
								PH1	PH2	PH3	PH1	PH2	PH3		

26. COMMENTS

DD FORM 2744 (BACK), MAY 96

CPSIA information can be obtained at www.ICGtesting.com
Printed in the USA
LVOW031404240812

295817LV00001B/16/A